Introduction

We all need to eat and drink to stay alive, so it is important that our food does not harm us in any way. Everyone who works with food has a special responsibility for safeguarding the health of consumers.

That responsibility involves making sure that food does not cause illness, injury or any other problem. *You* might not have the personal responsibility for every aspect of food handling mentioned in this book, but you still need to be aware of all the topics discussed because they could help you to avoid making someone ill.

Food Safety: First principles concentrates on the first principles of good practice. It covers the things you need to do to ensure that the food you make, serve or sell is perfectly safe to eat. All the principles are based on thorough scientific research, sound operational experience and legal requirements.

To help to make the principles straightforward there is a section of **key words** in every chapter. These are the words and phrases that you need to understand and feel confident using. Throughout the book you'll also find **key points** to keep in mind whenever you are working with food. There is also a **summary** at the end of each chapter which provides a useful reminder for your everyday work and may also help you to revise for a food safety examination.

Chapter 1
The importance of food safety

Food safety protects consumers' health and well-being by safeguarding food from anything that could harm them. High standards of food safety enable everyone to enjoy their food without illness, injury or other problems, but poor standards can lead to all kinds of harm – and even death. This chapter looks at the impact of illnesses caused by food and introduces the part that food handlers play in food safety.

Consumer expectations

Consumers want food that is fit to eat, and food safety is high on their list of concerns. They expect food handlers to do everything possible to keep food safe and wholesome.

The impact of illness

Food poisoning is caused by eating contaminated food. Even mild symptoms can be unpleasant, while severe symptoms can cause considerable discomfort and could be life threatening.

High standards of food safety bring important benefits to everyone – consumers, employees, business proprietors and the community in general. But there are high 'costs' from poor food safety including pain and distress for individuals, the loss of business profits and reputation and the public costs of medical care.

The number of recorded cases of food poisoning in the UK has dropped from record-high levels, but there are still thousands of cases every year as well as some deaths. It is important to remember that the true number of cases is probably far higher than the statistics. Most of the figures are reported by doctors, but not everyone sees a GP with symptoms such as an upset stomach, sickness or diarrhoea, so their illness is not officially recorded.

Key words

Case – the occurrence of an illness affecting one person.

Contaminated food – food that could be harmful to health because it contains something that should not be there.

Due diligence – a legal term describing the level of care that food companies must take over food safety.

Food – anything that people normally eat or drink, including ice and alcohol.

Food handler – anyone whose work involves food, or whose action or inaction could compromise the safety of food.

Food poisoning – a general term for an illness caused by eating contaminated food.

Food safety – the protection of consumer health and well-being by safeguarding food from anything that could cause harm.

Hazard (to food) – anything that could cause harm to a consumer.

Legislation – the general term for laws, regulations and directives.

Risk – the likelihood that harm will be caused.

Symptoms – the signs of illness.

Food should be wholesome and fit to eat

Benefits of effective food safety

- Satisfied customers.
- A good reputation.
- Loyal customers.
- Less food wastage and controlled running costs.
- A pleasant place to work.
- Compliance with food safety laws.
- Better job security.

Costs of poor food safety

- Food poisoning.
- A bad reputation.
- Customer complaints and possible loss of profit.
- Higher running costs because food has to be thrown away.
- Poor working conditions.
- Legal action and penalties.
- Possible redundancies and closure of the business.

Key points

- Food safety protects everyone.
- Food safety involves protecting food from anything that could harm consumer health and well-being.
- Poor standards of food safety threaten health, reputations, profits and jobs.
- Food poisoning is caused by eating contaminated food.
- Contaminated food is harmful to health because it contains something that should not be there.

Food safety and the law

As food safety is so important to everyone, the people who work with food have legal, ethical and economic responsibilities for keeping food safe to eat.

Rules covering the handling of food have existed for centuries. In modern times laws have been developed to cover every aspect of the handling and sale of food. Generally speaking, the legislation aims to protect consumers from illness and injury by requiring food to be wholesome and fit to eat.

The approach to food safety required by law is to *anticipate* food safety problems before they actually occur and to take appropriate steps to prevent them. There is a recognised system, known as the Hazard Analysis and Critical Control Point (HACCP), for doing so.

By law, food companies must analyse the food safety hazards (the *possibility* of harm) involved in their type of work and take steps to control the risks (the *likelihood* of harm) from them. The overall aim is to minimise the risk that harm will be caused. Companies must keep a constant check on the effectiveness of the controls they put in place and make any necessary adjustments to the way work is carried out.

There is also a legal requirement for companies working with food to take every reasonable care in all food safety issues. This can usually be achieved by following good working practice. Responsible companies also keep good records, such as a record of your training, so that they can demonstrate their 'due diligence' (reasonable care) if they ever needed to do so – for instance if there was an outbreak of illness connected to the business.

Companies have specific legal obligations to provide various essential food safety facilities, such as hand basins for your personal hygiene. They must also ensure that everyone who deals with food as part of his or her job and anyone else whose work could affect food – such as cleaning staff, engineers and delivery drivers – are supervised and given appropriate training for the work they do.

Responsible companies keep good records

Staff should be supervised and given appropriate training

Key points

- No one wants to eat contaminated food and the law says that people who work with food must protect food from contamination.
- Food establishments have a legal duty to produce food that is wholesome and safe to eat.
- It is against the law to serve or sell food that could injure health.

Your part in food safety

If you deal with food as part of your job, you are recognised as a *food handler* and are responsible for doing everything possible to keep food safe. This is a *legal* responsibility.

You are not expected to memorise every detail of the law, but you do need to understand how the law affects the way you work. There is more about this and good working practice throughout the book. In general, your part in food safety is likely to include:

- keeping yourself and your workplace clean
- protecting food from anything that could lead to illness or harm
- following good personal hygiene habits, such as washing your hands before handling food
- staying alert to food safety hazards – the possibility of harm
- following the rules for food safety in your workplace
- working with care
- telling your supervisor or manager about anything that you think could affect the safety of food.

As a food handler you are responsible for doing everything possible to keep food safe.

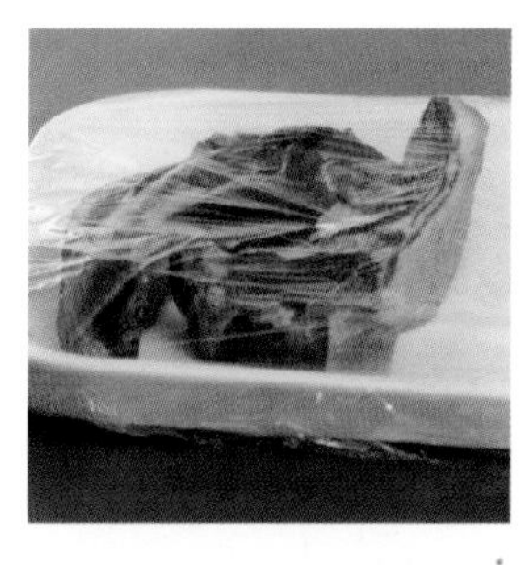

You must take action to protect the safety of food

Key point

- As a food handler you are responsible for doing everything possible to keep food safe.

Summary

1. Food safety involves protecting food from anything that could harm consumer health and well-being.

2. Food safety protects everyone.

3. Poor standards of food safety threaten health, reputations, profits and jobs.

4. Food poisoning is caused by eating contaminated food.

5. Contaminated food is harmful to health because it contains something that should not be there.

6. No one wants to eat contaminated food and the law says that people who work with food must protect food from contamination.

7. Food establishments have a legal duty to produce food that is wholesome and safe to eat.

8. It is against the law to serve or sell food that could injure health.

9. As a food handler you are responsible for doing everything possible to keep food safe.

Chapter 2
Hazards to food

Hazards to food are anything that could harm consumers by causing illness, injury or discomfort. The hazards include micro-organisms, physical objects and chemicals. There are many possible hazards to food at each of the stages from field to fork. As a food handler, you need to help to stop the possibility of harm from becoming actual harm. A crucial step is to prevent contamination. This chapter outlines food hazards and how they become a direct threat to health through food contamination.

Key words

Allergen – a food or ingredient that is perfectly safe for most people to eat, but which causes an allergic reaction in particular individuals.

Bacteria – simple, microscopic life forms that are responsible for causing most cases of food poisoning. The word 'bacteria' indicates more than one 'bacterium'.

Contaminant – any substance or object in food that makes the food harmful or objectionable.

Contaminated food – food that could be harmful to health because it contains something that should not be there.

Contamination – the presence in food of any harmful or objectionable substance or object.

Micro-organism (or microbe) – a very small (micro) life form (organism), such as bacteria, viruses, some fungi and microscopic parasites.

Parasite – a life form that lives uninvited on another creature.

Types of hazard

There are three types of hazard to food:

- **physical**
- **chemical**
- **biological**.

Examples of physical hazards include:

- broken glass or packaging materials, such as string
- fragments of shell or bone
- parts of machinery
- jewellery, hair and fingernails
- dust and dirt
- bodies of pests.

Examples of chemical hazards include:

- industrial or agricultural products in the food chain
- cleaning chemicals used in food premises
- pest bait in food premises
- dissolved metals from inappropriate use of metal containers.

Examples of biological hazards include:

- bacteria that can cause illness or spoil food
- viruses
- fungi, such as mould and yeast, that can spoil food
- naturally occurring poisons, such as those found in some plants, fish and mushrooms
- microscopic parasites.

Key point

- There are three types of hazard to food: physical, chemical and biological.

How the threat to health starts

Even the simplest food could go through several stages before reaching the consumer's plate and there are many stages involved before some foods are sold. Among the stages could be growing, slaughtering, harvesting, catching, processing, packing, delivering, storing, preparing, cooking, displaying, selling and serving. As you can see from the lists on the previous page, there are hazards all around food. They exist in the natural world and they can be created by people. Hazards are a *possible* danger. They become an actual threat to consumer health when they are on or in food – in other words, when food is *contaminated*.

Contamination is the presence of something harmful or objectionable in food or drink. Contamination starts the events that lead to food poisoning. This is why food companies must watch out for hazards to food – the *possible* dangers – and take steps to stop the possibility of harm from becoming *actual* harm.

Chapter 2 looks at physical and chemical hazards, while Chapter 3 considers biological hazards. As you'll see, there are very high risks to food safety from biological hazards because of the way in which bacteria and other 'bugs' live and reproduce. You also need to know about allergens – foods or ingredients that could harm particular individuals.

Key points

- There are hazards all around food.
- Hazards have the potential to cause harm to all consumers.
- The events that lead to food poisoning start with contamination – the presence in food of something harmful or objectionable.
- Controlling contamination is a crucial way to prevent illness.
- Some products and ingredients can cause illness in particular individuals who have an allergy to the food.

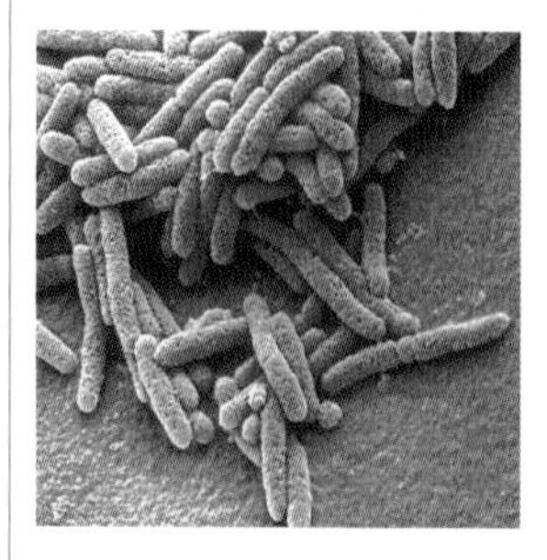

Contamination starts the events that lead to food poisoning

Controlling contamination is crucial to preventing illness

Allergens

Contaminated food can affect anyone who eats it. There are also foods that are hazardous to a small group of people. These foods are described as allergens. They are foods or ingredients, such as peanuts, that are perfectly safe for most people to eat but can cause illness and even death to people who cannot tolerate that food. There is more about allergies in Chapters 3 and 5.

Summary

1. There are three types of hazard: physical, chemical and biological.

2. There are hazards all around food.

3. Hazards have the potential to cause harm to all consumers.

4. The events that lead to food poisoning start with contamination – the presence in food of something harmful or objectionable.

5. Controlling contamination is a crucial way to prevent illness.

6. Some products and ingredients can cause illness in particular individuals who have an allergy to the food.

Chapter 3
Physical and chemical hazards

Biological hazards cause most of the illnesses linked to food, but physical and chemical hazards can also lead to injury, illness and considerable consumer anxiety. This chapter outlines the sources and consequences of typical physical and chemical hazards.

Key word

Source – where something comes from.

Physical hazards

No one wants a fly in their soup, or any other kind of physical contaminant in their food. Physical contamination causes considerable consumer dissatisfaction and complaint, probably because the contaminant can be seen, unlike most forms of biological and chemical contamination.

Among the problems from physical contaminants are cuts, bleeding, choking, infection and broken teeth. Even if consumers are not injured by a physical contaminant, some people can be so upset that they are sick or have nightmares.

Key point

- Physical contamination causes considerable consumer dissatisfaction and complaint.

In the natural world

Some physical hazards are a natural part of a food, such as leaves, twigs, shell, scale or bone, so they are likely to be present in many food premises. Some foods are sold 'whole' or with a warning that the food may contain bones, for example. It is up to consumers to watch out for anything that could cause them harm in these foods. For other foods consumers expect the food company to remove all physical contaminants, and this is backed up by the law.

Fruit, vegetables, grain (such as rice) and pulses (such as chick peas and lentils) usually carry soil and dirt. These are physical contaminants that can easily contaminate other foods. This is why you need to wash all raw food well away from other foods that are ready to be consumed or packaged.

Soil and dirt can easily contaminate other foods

Key points

- Fruit, vegetables, rice and pulses carry soil and dirt.
- Wash all raw food before use and be careful not to contaminate other food in the process.

At all stages from field to fork

There are many stages when physical hazards can become physical contaminants and cause injury or distress. Food handlers are themselves a major source of physical contamination, including hair, fingernails, buttons, badges, pen tops, plasters and jewellery. This is why they must wear suitable protective clothing and must not wear jewellery (*see* Chapter 8).

Food packaging also creates physical hazards, including paper, string, staples and wood fragments. Ideally, the outer packaging of food should be removed in an area away from open food.

Poorly maintained buildings, equipment and machinery can be the source of contamination such as paint fragments, screws, nuts, bolts and metal shavings (*see* Chapter 9).

Ineffective cleaning can cause dirt and dust to contaminate food, while food waste and rubbish must be removed regularly to prevent contamination (*see* Chapter 10). Pests, such as insects and rodents, are also a source of physical contamination. Their bodies, eggs, droppings and nesting materials can all cause problems if there is not an effective system of pest control in place (*see* Chapter 11).

Key points

- Food handlers are a major source of physical contamination.
- Wear appropriate protective clothing and do not wear anything, such as jewellery, that could contaminate food.
- Keep food areas and food equipment clean and in good condition.
- Report any damage to premises and equipment that could cause contamination.
- Remove food waste and rubbish from food areas frequently throughout the day and dispose of it safely and hygienically.
- Report any signs of pests in the building.

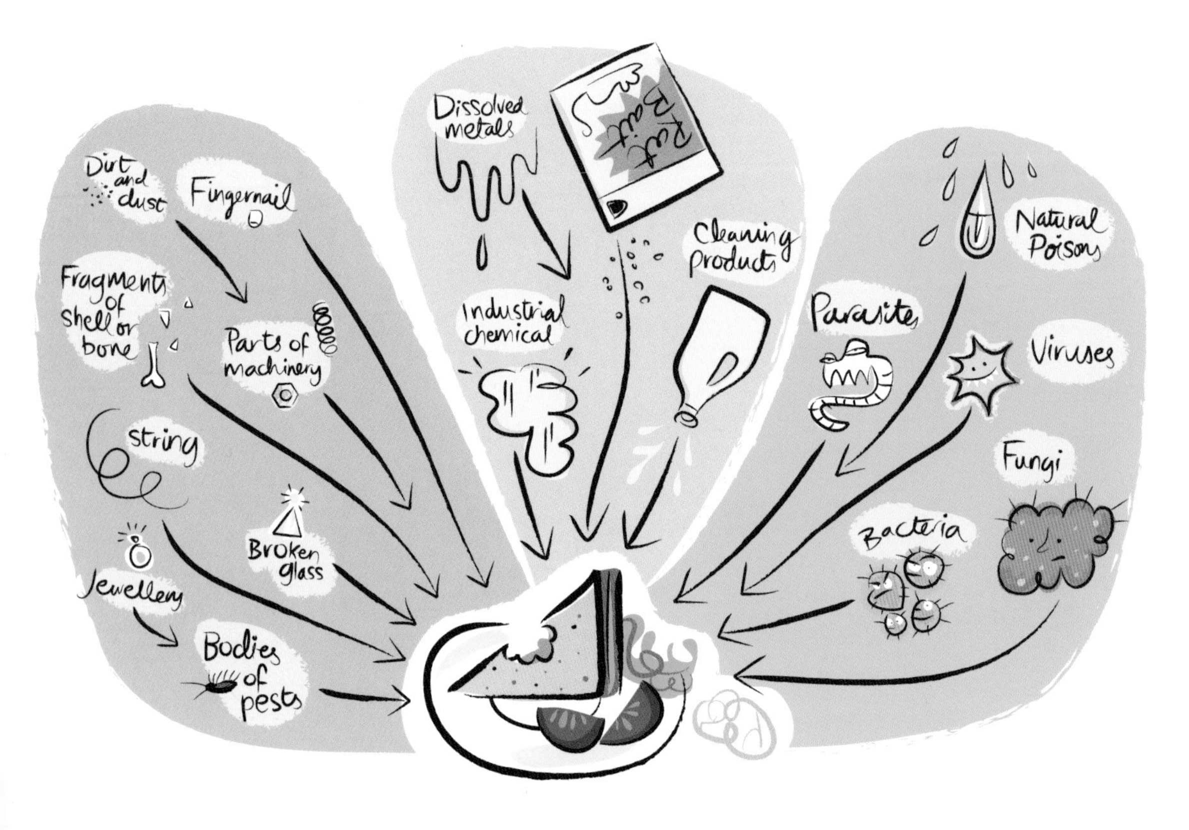

Allergens

Allergens are a hazard to anyone with an allergy to that food, even though the food is safe for most other people to eat. Among the foods that have been linked to allergies are:

- nuts (such as peanuts), seeds (such as sesame) and products made from them (such as salad dressings and cakes)
- shellfish and fish
- milk and dairy products
- food colourants and flavour enhancers
- chocolate
- fruit
- flour.

Foods linked to allergies include nuts and milk and dairy products

Key points

- Allergens are a hazard to anyone with an allergy to that food.
- Care needs to be taken to avoid accidental contamination by foods linked to allergies.

Chemical hazards

Harmful chemicals can be accidentally added to food from a number of sources and in several ways. These include:

- **chemical hazards in the environment** – such as poisonous metals from rubbish dumps and the by-products of industrial processing
- **agricultural or veterinary residues** – such as traces of pesticides, fertilisers, animal antibiotics or growth hormones
- **incorrect quantities of additives** – such as food colours or flavour enhancers
- **inappropriate workplace practices** – such as the careless use of lubricants or cleaning products, or contact reactions from the use of unsuitable food containers used for acidic foods.

The symptoms of some types of chemical poisoning, such as vomiting, diarrhoea and abdominal pain, are similar to many symptoms of food poisoning (*see* Chapter 5). But some other forms of chemical poisoning take months and even years to develop as people eat very small quantities of a harmful chemical over a long period. Life-threatening conditions can occur including damage to the brain, nervous system, kidneys and liver.

Key point

- Sources of chemical contamination include the environment, agricultural or veterinary residues, food additives and inappropriate workplace practices.

Careless use of cleaning products can cause chemical contamination

Prevention

Someone in your company is responsible for buying food from a reputable supplier and for making checks on physical and chemical contaminants in foods and ingredients. You can play your part by:

- carrying out appropriate food safety measures such as sieving and washing
- watching out for physical contaminants in food and following your workplace rules for dealing with them
- reporting to your supervisor any hazards that you spot that could result in food contamination
- working safely with cleaning chemicals (*see* Chapter 10).

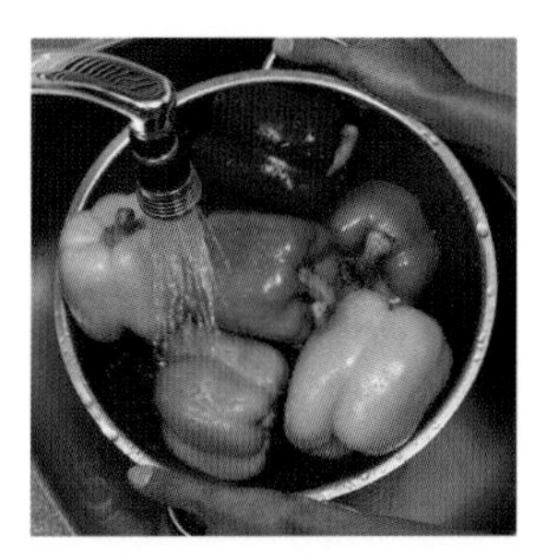

Sieving and washing foods can help to prevent physical and chemical contamination

Key point

- Report to your supervisor any hazards that you spot that could result in food contamination.

Summary

1. Physical contamination causes considerable consumer dissatisfaction and complaint.
2. Fruit, vegetables, rice and pulses carry soil and dirt.
3. Wash all raw food before use and be careful not to contaminate other food in the process.
4. Food handlers are a major source of physical contamination.
5. Wear appropriate protective clothing and do not wear anything, such as jewellery, that could contaminate food.
6. Keep food areas and food equipment clean and in good condition.
7. Report any damage to premises and equipment that could cause contamination.
8. Remove food waste and rubbish from food areas frequently throughout the day and dispose of it safely and hygienically.
9. Report any signs of pests in the building.
10. Allergens are a hazard to anyone with an allergy to that food.
11. Care needs to be taken to avoid accidental contamination by foods linked to allergies.
12. Sources of chemical contamination include the environment, agricultural or veterinary residues, food additives and inappropriate workplace practices.
13. Report to your supervisor any hazards that you spot that could result in food contamination.

Chapter 4
Biological hazards

Biological hazards are the main cause of food poisoning and most cases of illness are caused by bacteria – tiny life forms that live on and in our bodies and throughout the natural world. Other biological causes of illness linked to food include viruses, parasites and poisonous fish, plants and fungi. This chapter introduces the harmful bacteria and other biological hazards that are of concern to everyone who works with food.

Key words

Bacteriology – the study of bacteria.

Binary fission – the process by which a bacterium multiplies by splitting in two.

High-risk foods – ready-to-eat foods which are ideal for the multiplication of food poisoning organisms such as bacteria.

Multiply – to reproduce (increase in numbers). Bacteria multiply by the process of binary fission.

Pathogen – an organism that causes disease. Pathogenic bacteria cause illnesses such as food poisoning.

Potable – water that has been treated so that it is safe to drink.

Spoilage – the process of causing damage. Spoilage bacteria make food perish.

Spore – the protective form of some bacteria that helps them to survive adverse conditions such as cooking or drying.

Toxin – a poison produced by some bacteria and moulds.

Vehicle of contamination – hands, spoons or anything else that can carry micro-organisms onto food, causing contamination.

Bacteria

Bacteria are single-celled micro-organisms that are too small to see without the help of a powerful microscope. Even when food is heavily contaminated, it is usually impossible to detect bacteria by sight, smell or taste.

Bacteria are found throughout the natural world and survive under many conditions. Although they are responsible for most cases of food poisoning, it is important to remember that not all types of bacteria are harmful. Indeed, most types are beneficial and humans would find it difficult to survive without them.

Helpful bacteria (sometimes known as 'friendly' bacteria) help us to grow crops; make foods such as yoghurt, cheese and fizzy drinks; digest the food we eat; treat sewage to make it safe; create medicines; and manufacture laundry and cleaning products.

The very small proportion of *harmful* bacteria can cause a great deal of harm. They include *pathogenic* bacteria that cause illnesses, and *spoilage* bacteria that make food perish rapidly.

Key points

- Biological hazards are the main cause of food poisoning and most cases of illness are caused by bacteria.
- Not all types of bacteria are harmful.
- Bacteria can be divided into three types: *helpful* bacteria, *pathogenic* bacteria and *spoilage* bacteria.

Some bacteria help us to make food such as yoghurt

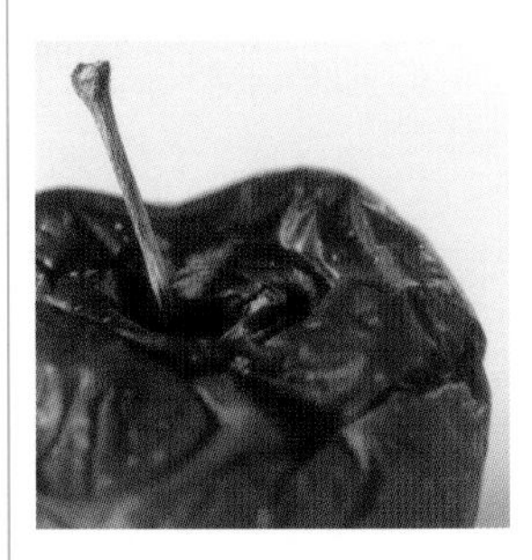

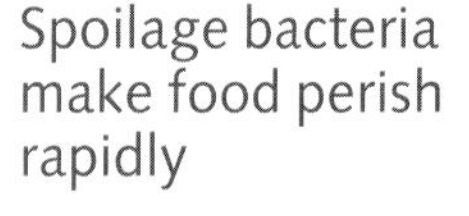

Spoilage bacteria make food perish rapidly

Raw food is a significant source of contamination

Pathogenic bacteria

Pathogenic means 'disease-causing' and these types of bacteria are responsible for most cases of food poisoning and food-borne illness.

Where pathogenic bacteria come from

There are many sources of bacterial contamination.

Raw food

Vegetables and foods of animal origin – meat, poultry, fish, shellfish and eggs – are significant sources of contamination. Bacteria are naturally present in animal intestines. When animals are slaughtered, the skin and flesh may be accidentally contaminated by these bacteria. If the meat is then minced, for burgers for instance, the bacteria can be spread throughout the food.

Water

Untreated and incorrectly treated sources of drinking water, such as rivers, lakes and reservoirs, can carry the pathogenic micro-organisms that cause food-borne illness. So, all water used in food preparation and recipes must be potable – in other words, it must have been treated to make it safe to drink.

Soil

There are many bacteria living in the soil. They can cause illness if raw food is not washed thoroughly before it is eaten.

People

Pathogenic bacteria can be found on human skin and in the ears, nose, throat and hair. They are also in cuts, pimples and boils. Food handlers can spread bacteria by touching their faces, hair or other parts of their body before handling food; by not washing their hands after going to the bathroom; or by coughing or sneezing near food.

Air, dust, dirt and food waste

The air carries dust and dirt containing millions of microscopic particles of dead skin, food and other debris covered in pathogenic bacteria that can settle on uncovered food. Bacteria from food waste (and from the pests that the scraps may attract) can contaminate food if the waste is not disposed of properly.

Pests and pets

Insects, such as flies and cockroaches, and animals, including mice, dogs, cats, hamsters, amphibians and reptiles, all carry harmful micro-organisms on and in their bodies.

Bacteria can be spread throughout a product by processes such as mincing

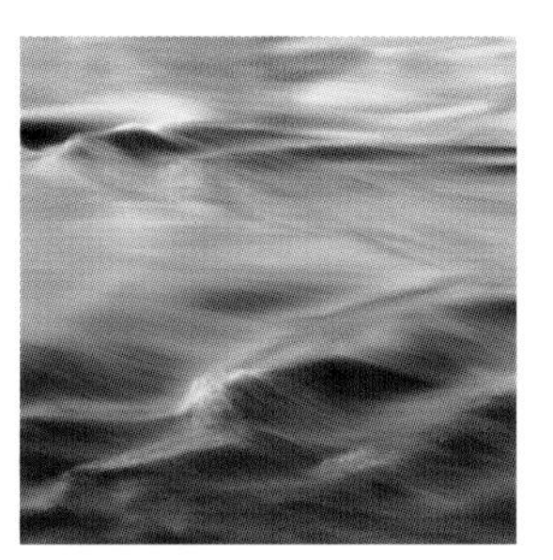

Water can carry pathogenic micro-organisms

Key points

- Pathogenic bacteria cause most of the cases of illness from food.
- As bacteria exist in the environment – in water, soil and the air – and on and inside animals, many raw foods are contaminated with pathogenic bacteria before they reach your workplace.
- Food handlers' bodies carry bacteria.
- Keep all food covered until it is needed for preparation or sale.

How pathogenic bacteria are spread

Pathogenic bacteria cause most of the cases of illness from food. Careless or inappropriate food handling may *add* bacteria to food – from unwashed hands, for example. Poor practices can also *spread* bacteria from one food to another. This can happen when a contaminated food is allowed to *touch* an uncontaminated food or to drip onto it. It can also be transported by vehicles of contamination.

Vehicles of contamination

Bacteria can move, but they cannot travel far on their own. Anything that enables bacteria to travel is referred to as a 'vehicle of contamination'. People, animals, equipment and utensils are the most usual vehicles of contamination, in particular:

- hands
- work surfaces, containers, crockery and cutlery
- utensils and equipment, such as chopping boards and dish cloths
- any food-contact surface that has not been cleaned properly between uses.

Vehicles of contamination are often involved in causing cross-contamination.

Hands and cloths are common vehicles of cross-contamination

Cross-contamination

Cross-contamination occurs when pathogenic bacteria are transferred from a contaminated source, such as raw meat, to a high-risk food. A high-risk food is a ready-to-eat item that is ideal for bacteria to live on. Such foods are typically involved in food poisoning, which is why they are known as high-risk foods. As these foods cause most of the biggest food safety problems, you'll find more detailed information about them in Chapter 6.

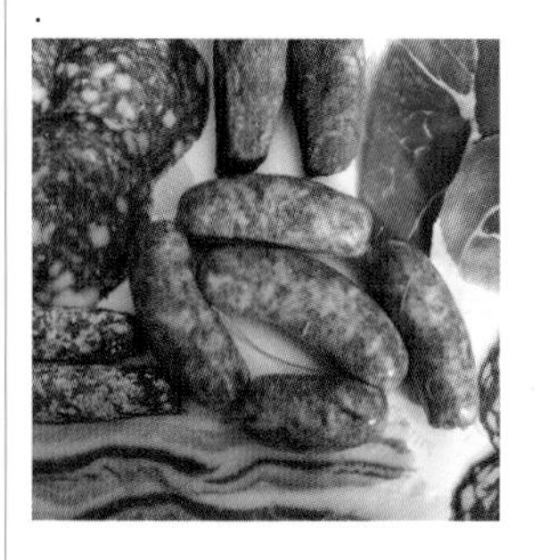

Cross-contamination – raw to cooked food

Key points

- Anything that touches food is a possible vehicle of contamination.
- Hands are a common vehicle of contamination.
- Follow strict personal hygiene habits while working with food.
- Do not touch your hair, or eat or drink in case you transfer bacteria from your head or mouth to food.
- Cross-contamination occurs when pathogenic bacteria are transferred from a contaminated source to a high-risk food.
- Wash your hands frequently and thoroughly.

Spoilage bacteria

Spoilage is the process by which food spoils or becomes unacceptable to eat. It is also known as decomposition, rotting, perishing, deteriorating and going bad.

Spoilage bacteria are present in the environment and cause contamination in the same way as pathogenic bacteria. As well as moulds and yeast, spoilage bacteria are responsible for making food spoil rapidly. This damages the quality of food, reduces its shelf life and, in some cases, can also cause illness.

Key point

- Spoilage bacteria can damage the quality of food, reduce its shelf life and cause illness.

How bacteria reproduce

Bacterial reproduction is usually referred to as *multiplication*. Bacteria multiply by dividing in two – a process known as *binary fission*. As each bacterium needs just 10 to 20 minutes to multiply in the right conditions, it is possible for just one bacterium to lead to the production of millions of bacteria within a few hours.

High numbers of pathogenic bacteria can cause food poisoning, while high numbers of spoilage bacteria make food perish quickly, so food handlers need to control the conditions that allow them to multiply. The ideal conditions for bacterial multiplication include food, moisture, warmth and time. They are discussed in greater detail in Chapter 5.

Key points

- Bacteria reproduce by multiplying.
- The ideal conditions for bacterial multiplication include food, moisture, warmth and time.

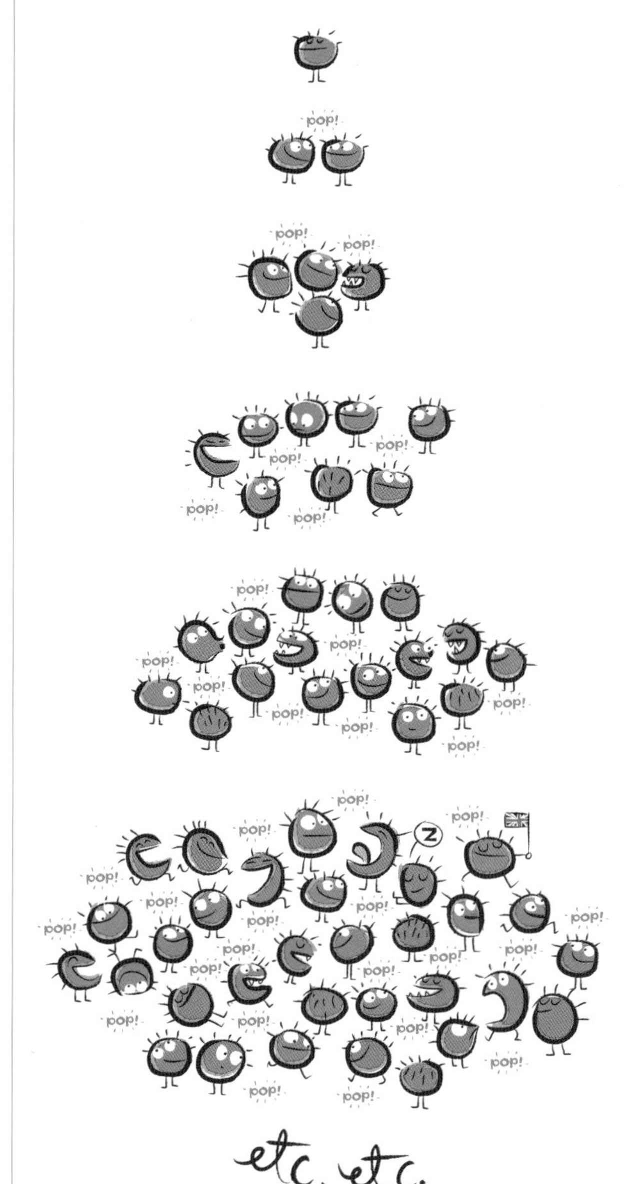

Other biological hazards

Apart from bacteria, other biological hazards to food include viruses, parasites and naturally poisonous plants, fish and fungi.

Viruses

Viruses are micro-organisms that are even smaller than bacteria. They are carried on food and water but do not need the food or moisture for their own survival. The main sources of viruses are sewage and polluted water. Although they can contaminate any type of food, they are usually associated with:

- water
- foods from water, such as shellfish
- raw food, such as salad leaves and raw vegetables.

Viruses can be spread by vehicles of contamination, such as hands. For example, food handlers can spread viruses to food if they fail to wash their hands thoroughly after going to the toilet.

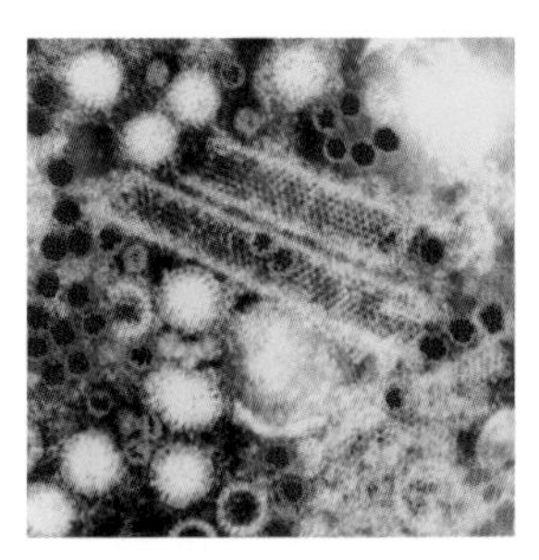

Norovirus is a common cause of food-borne illness

Key points

- Viruses are carried on food and water.
- The main sources of viruses are sewage and polluted water.

Parasites

Parasites are organisms that live on or in other organisms, such as fleas on dogs and cats. The parasites that cause illness from food include:

- microscopic types that live in water
- roundworms, flatworms and flukes that affect foods of animal origin, such as pork, beef and fish.

Meat and fish must be cooked thoroughly to kill any parasites present in the raw food.

Taenia saginata – a flatworm found in beef

Key points

- Parasites live on or in other organisms.
- Food must be cooked thoroughly to kill any parasites that are in raw food.

Naturally poisonous foods

Some foods are naturally poisonous to people. They include:

- red kidney beans, until they have been boiled for long enough
- rhubarb leaves
- castor beans
- parts of some fish in certain seasons – such as catfish roe
- some treated fish that have not been processed correctly – such as canned tuna, herring and mackerel
- some fungi – certain mushrooms and toadstools – are poisonous and some moulds can produce toxins (particular types of poison).

Food companies should buy these foods from reliable suppliers and take appropriate precautions, such as using only canned red kidney beans that have already been processed to make them safe to eat.

Some foods are safe to eat only after careful processing

Key point

- Some foods are naturally poisonous – for example red kidney beans – and must be carefully processed so that they are safe to eat.

Biological hazards – your role

Even the simplest or least processed food could go through several stages before reaching the consumer's plate and some products go through many stages before they are sold. Everyone who deals with the food at any stage has a responsibility to stay alert to biological hazards and to prevent contamination.

You may not be involved in all the actions needed to prevent contamination at your workplace – for instance, you may not be responsible for choosing reputable suppliers. However, it is important to understand the general principles involved. Never be shy to ask your supervisor if you are unsure about how to do something. Always tell your supervisor if you think you have spotted a hazard to food safety.

Find out the food safety rules in your workplace and follow them carefully. For example, many companies provide colour-coded preparation equipment, such as chopping boards, cleaning cloths and knives, to help to prevent cross-contamination. Each colour is designated for a particular use. For instance, red could indicate that a chopping board must be used for raw red meat only, while green could indicate use for vegetables only. In some other companies, such as poultry processing plants, staff have different coloured uniforms which indicate the processing areas they are permitted to enter. Some retailers insist that staff can handle either raw food or cooked food, but not both.

Key points

- Everyone who deals with the food at any stage has a responsibility to stay alert to biological hazards and to prevent contamination.
- If possible, use separate equipment and utensils for the preparation of raw meats, poultry and fish and other foods.

Summary

1. Biological hazards are the main cause of food poisoning and most cases of illness are caused by bacteria.

2. Not all types of bacteria are harmful.

3. Bacteria can be divided into three types: *helpful* bacteria, *pathogenic* bacteria and *spoilage* bacteria.

4. Pathogenic bacteria cause most of the cases of illness from food.

5. As bacteria exist in the environment – in water, soil and the air – and on and inside animals, many raw foods are contaminated with pathogenic bacteria before they reach your workplace.

6. Food handlers' bodies carry bacteria.

7. Keep all food covered until it is needed for preparation or sale.

8. Anything that touches food is a possible vehicle of contamination.

9. Hands are a common vehicle of contamination.

10. Follow strict personal hygiene habits while working with food.

11. Do not touch your hair, or eat or drink in case you transfer bacteria from your head or mouth to food.

12. Cross-contamination occurs when pathogenic bacteria are transferred from a contaminated source to a high-risk food.

13. Wash your hands frequently and thoroughly.

14. Spoilage bacteria can damage the quality of food, reduce its shelf life and cause illness.

15. Bacteria reproduce by multiplying.

16. The ideal conditions for bacterial multiplication include food, moisture, warmth and time.

17. Viruses are carried on food and water.

18. The main sources of viruses are sewage and polluted water.

19. Parasites live on or in other organisms.

20. Food must be cooked thoroughly to kill any parasites that are in raw food.

21. Some foods are naturally poisonous – for example red kidney beans – and must be carefully processed so that they are safe to eat.

22. Everyone who deals with the food at any stage has a responsibility to stay alert to biological hazards and to prevent contamination.

23. If possible, use separate equipment and utensils for the preparation of raw meats, poultry and fish and other foods.

Chapter 5
Illness from food

Eating or drinking contaminated food can cause injury or illness. Most illnesses linked to food are caused by bacteria which, at the very least, cause discomfort. This chapter focuses on the main features of illnesses from biologically contaminated food. It also considers allergies to food.

Illnesses linked to food

There are two types of illness from contaminated food that can affect anyone. They are :

- **food poisoning**
- **food-borne illness.**

A small, but growing, number of people are also affected by food allergies.

Food poisoning

Food poisoning is caused by eating food contaminated by one of the following:

- pathogenic bacteria that are living on the food
- harmful substances, such as poisonous plants, fish or fungi; some chemicals and metals; toxins (poisons) from certain types of mould (on nuts, for example).

Food-borne illness

A food-borne illness is caused by consuming food or water that is carrying harmful micro-organisms, such as a virus or parasites.

Key point

- Food poisoning and food-borne illness are types of illness caused by eating contaminated food.

Key words

Allergy (to food) – a type of intolerance to a food that causes the body's immune system to react as if the body were under attack.

Duration – the time that an illness lasts.

Food-borne illness – an illness caused by micro-organisms carried by food or water.

Food poisoning – a general term for an illness caused by eating contaminated food.

Nausea – feeling sick.

Onset or **incubation period** – the time it takes for the symptoms of an illness to start after contaminated food has been eaten.

Symptoms – the signs of illness.

Vomiting – being sick.

Food poisoning

Pathogenic bacteria are the most common cause of food poisoning. Such bacteria include:

- *Salmonella*
- *Staphylococcus aureus*
- *Clostridium perfringens*
- *Clostridium botulinum*
- *Bacillus cereus.*

Bacterial food poisoning typically occurs in the following circumstances:

- a high-risk food – the type that cause most food safety problems (*see* Chapter 6) – is contaminated
- the food is kept in conditions, such as a warm room, that allow the bacteria to multiply to levels that cause illness
- the bacteria are not destroyed, for instance by adequate cooking, so that they go on living on the food
- the food is eaten.

How the bacteria make you ill

When your body detects that you have eaten something harmful, it tries to get rid of the food by the quickest method. This means that the most common symptoms of food poisoning are:

- abdominal pain
- nausea (feeling sick)
- vomiting
- diarrhoea.

Other signs of illness may include a fever and headache.

Most pathogenic bacteria make you ill when they have been inside your body for a while – between 8 and 36 hours. However, some bacteria, such as *Staphylococcus aureus*, produce toxins (poisons) in food even before you eat it, so you are likely to feel ill fairly soon after eating. This onset period could be just one hour or up to six hours later. There are also bacteria that make you ill as a result of forming spores – a protective form of some types of bacteria that enables them to survive the harsh conditions, such as cooking, that would otherwise destroy them.

The illness usually lasts for 24 to 48 hours, but it can continue for a week or more. Food poisoning can be life-threatening for some people – see 'People at risk' on page 28.

Key points

- Bacterial food poisoning is caused by bacteria that live on high-risk food and multiply to levels that cause illness.
- Large numbers of pathogenic micro-organisms are needed to cause food poisoning. In contrast, it takes only very small numbers of pathogenic micro-organisms to cause a food-borne illness.
- The most common symptoms of food poisoning are abdominal pain, diarrhoea, vomiting and nausea.

Food-borne illness

A food-borne illness is caused by micro-organisms that are *carried* by food or, particularly, water. Contamination by only a few of these microbes may cause a food-borne illness, so it is especially important for food companies to buy food from reputable suppliers and for food handlers to prevent contamination.

Food-borne illness is caused by bacteria such as:

- *Campylobacter* – one of the most common causes of all bacterial illnesses from food
- *Escherichia coli* O157 *(E. coli)*
- *Listeria*
- the bacteria that cause typhoid and dysentery.

Other causes of food-borne illness are viruses – such Hepatitis and Norovirus – and parasites, such as tapeworms.

Symptoms

Some of the symptoms of food-borne illness can be similar to those of food poisoning. For example, Norovirus causes vomiting. Other food-borne illnesses have symptoms such as kidney failure or paralysis that can lead to death.

It can take days, weeks or even months for the symptoms to appear. The illness can last for a day or so, or continue for many years with serious long-term health problems.

Key points

- Food-borne illnesses are caused by pathogenic micro-organisms that are carried by food and water.
- The symptoms of some food-borne illnesses can be similar to those of food poisoning. Other severe symptoms include paralysis and kidney failure.

Campylobacter can be found in raw meat, offal and poultry

E.coli can be found in beef – particularly minced beef

Listeria can be found in unpasteurized soft cheese

Salad washed in dirty water can also cause food-borne illness

Examples of food poisoning and food-borne illness

Food poisoning

Pathogenic bacteria	Common source	Linked to food	Typical symptoms	Average onset time
Salmonella	Human and animal gut, pests and sewage	Raw and uncooked poultry, eggs and meat; and raw milk	Abdominal pain, diarrhoea, vomiting, fever	12–36 hours
Staphylococcus aureus	Human body – especially skin, nose, mouth, cuts and boils – and raw milk	Cold meats, raw milk and diary products, anything touched by hand	Abdominal pain, or abdominal cramp, vomiting, low temperature	1–6 hours
Clostridium perfringens	Animal and human excreta, soil, dust, insects and raw meat	Cooked meat and poultry	Abdominal pain, diarrhoea	12–18 hours
Clostridium botulinum (Botulism)	Soil and water	Fish, meat, vegetables, smoked fish, canned fish and corned beef, hazelnut purée	Difficulties in breathing and swallowing, paralysis	12–36 hours
Bacillus cereus	Cereals, soil and dust	Cereals (especially rice)	Abdominal pain, some diarrhoea, vomiting	1–5 hours or 8-16 hours depending on the form of the food poisoning

Food-borne illness

Pathogenic bacteria	Common source	Linked to food	Typical symptoms	Average onset time
Campylobacter jejuni	Animals, sewage and untreated water	Raw poultry, meat and milk; untreated water	Diarrhoea, often bloody, abdominal pain, nausea, fever	48–60 hours
Escherichia coli O157 (*E. coli*)	Human and animal gut, sewage, water and raw meat	Beef (especially minced) and other meat; raw milk; untreated water	Abdominal pain, fever, diarrhoea, vomiting, kidney damage or failure	12–24 hours or longer
Listeria	Soil, water, sewage, people	Soft cheese, cheese made from unpasteurized milk, salad vegetables and pâté	Symptoms like 'flu	1–70 days
Shigella (Bacillary dysentery)	People	Water, milk, salad vegetables	Diarrhoea, sometimes bloody, fever, abdominal pain, vomiting	1–7 days

Examples of food poisoning and food-borne illness

The chart on the previous page is included mainly for reference, as you are not expected to memorise every detail of every illness linked to food. Even so, it is useful to learn some examples of foods associated with particularly micro-organisms – chicken and *Salmonella*, for example – and examples of average onset times, such as those for *Staphylococcus* and *Salmonella*.

People at risk from illnesses linked to food

Anyone can be affected by food poisoning or food-borne illness but some people are affected particularly badly if they become ill, and they could even die from the illness. The people in this 'at risk' group are:

- the very young
- the elderly
- people who are ill or convalescing or who have weakened immunity to disease
- pregnant women and their unborn baby.

Key point

- People who are very young, very old, pregnant, ill or recovering from illness are particularly at risk from food poisoning or food-borne illness.

Food allergies

Some people are particularly sensitive to certain foods, such as nuts and seeds, and become ill after eating products that are harmless to others. This is a food allergy – a type of intolerance to food that makes the immune system react as if the body were under attack.

Allergic reactions can occur within minutes of eating just a small amount of a food or ingredient, or can take several hours to develop. Some reactions are mild, but others may cause death if medical treatment is not given rapidly.

There is a wide range of symptoms from food allergies, including some, such as sickness, diarrhoea and abdominal cramp, similar to the symptoms of food poisoning. Other allergic reactions include rashes; tingling of the lips, tongue and throat; swelling of the throat and mouth; and difficulty in breathing or speaking.

One type of allergic reaction, described as anaphylactic shock, is life-threatening. The symptoms may start with a mild reaction but can lead to a swelling in the throat, difficulty in breathing, a dramatic drop in blood pressure, collapse and unconsciousness.

Most people who have a food allergy know what to avoid, but often need help in identifying the ingredients used. They need to be able to trust the information given to them. Check with your supervisor exactly what the ingredients are in a product and ensure that you give consumers the correct information.

You must also ensure that you do not contaminate other foods with allergens. The steps involved include washing your hands after handling allergens, segregating allergens from other ingredients and ensuring that utensils and equipment used for allergens do not become vehicles of contamination to foods that are intended to be allergen free.

Customers need clear and accurate information about ingredients linked to food allergies

Key points

- Food allergies affect a small group of people with symptoms that can be life threatening.
- Allergic reactions to food make the immune system react as if the body were under attack.
- Foods and ingredients that are linked to food allergies need to be separated from foods that are intended to be allergen free.
- Consumers need accurate information about food allergens.

Summary

1. Food poisoning and food-borne illness are types of illness caused by eating contaminated food.

2. Bacterial food poisoning is caused by bacteria that live on high-risk food and multiply to levels that cause illness.

3. Large numbers of pathogenic micro-organisms are needed to cause food poisoning. In contrast, it takes only very small numbers of pathogenic micro-organisms to cause a food-borne illness.

4. The most common symptoms of food poisoning are abdominal pain, diarrhoea, vomiting and nausea.

5. Food-borne illnesses are caused by pathogenic micro-organisms that are carried by food and water.

6. The symptoms of some food-borne illnesses can be similar to those of food poisoning. Other severe symptoms include paralysis and kidney failure.

7. People who are very young, very old, pregnant, ill or recovering from illness are particularly at risk from food poisoning or food-borne illness.

8. Food allergies affect a small group of people with symptoms that can be life threatening.

9. Allergic reactions to food make the immune system react as if the body were under attack.

10. Foods and ingredients that are linked to food allergies need to be separated from foods that are intended to be allergen free.

11. Consumers need accurate information about food allergens.

Chapter 6
High-risk food

Some products, described as high-risk foods, are more likely to cause food poisoning than others. This is because they help to provide the ideal conditions for bacterial multiplication to the levels that cause illness. This chapter considers these foods in greater detail.

Key words

Ambient temperature – ordinary room temperature. (Strictly speaking, 'ambient' means the surrounding temperature.)

Dehydrate – to dry out.

Danger zone – the temperature range (5°C to 63°C) most suitable for bacterial multiplication.

Dormant – a period of inactivity when bacteria do not multiply.

Ready-to-eat foods – foods which are not prepared or treated immediately before eating in a way that would destroy pathogenic bacteria.

Identifying high-risk foods

Food handlers need to recognise high-risk foods so that they can take all the necessary steps to prevent them causing illness. There are three important things to remember – high-risk foods:

- are ready to eat
- help to provide the ideal conditions for bacterial multiplication to the levels that cause illness
- require strict time and temperature control.

Ready to eat

Most high-risk foods are ready for eating. As the name suggests, ready-to-eat foods can be eaten straight away, without extra preparation (such as additional washing or full cooking) that would destroy pathogens just before the food is eaten.

Food and moisture

Most high-risk foods are also moist and full of protein. These are conditions that favour bacterial multiplication when the food spends enough time in a warm environment. There's more about food and moisture, plus warmth and time on pages 32 and 33.

Time and temperature control

As most high-risk foods are moist and full of protein, food handlers must ensure that these foods spend as short a time as possible in warm conditions. This time and temperature control is a major step in preventing food poisoning, so you'll find plenty more information about it in the rest of this chapter and those that follow (in particular Chapter 7).

Key point

- High-risk foods are ready-to-eat foods. They are moist and protein-rich, providing the ideal conditions for the multiplication of pathogens to the levels that cause food poisoning when the food spends enough time in warm conditions.

Typical high-risk foods

High-risk foods may be of animal or plant origin. They may be raw, or have been cooked at an earlier stage so that they can be eaten cold or reheated just before consumption. The main high-risk foods are:

- cooked meat and cooked poultry
- cooked meat products – such as stews, gravy and soups made with meat or meat stock
- meat or fish pâtés and spreads
- milk and eggs, and uncooked and lightly-cooked dishes made with them – such as mayonnaise and hollandaise sauces and mousses
- shellfish and seafood – including prawns, shrimps, mussels, oysters, crab, lobster and scampi
- cooked rice
- delicatessen products such as soft cheese
- prepared salads, such as salad leaves, and vegetables.

Ideal conditions for multiplication

It is essential to understand the conditions that enable bacteria to multiply to levels that cause food poisoning. They are a combination of four main requirements:

- **food**
- **moisture**
- **warmth**
- **time.**

When bacteria spend enough time on the right types of food at a temperature in the danger zone (*see* below), they can quickly multiply to the levels that cause illness.

Food

Like all living things, bacteria need nutrients. Although different types of food poisoning bacteria can live on a range of foods, most prefer something that is both moist and high in protein, such as those listed above. These foods support the multiplication of bacteria even if they are cooked thoroughly and served cold later.

Moisture

Food poisoning bacteria need moisture to stay alive, and they cannot multiply in dried foods. However, as soon as liquid is added to foods, such as dried eggs and powdered milk, the reconstituted products provide ideal conditions for bacteria to multiply.

In contrast, quantities of salt or sugar (in foods such as savoury biscuits and bacon, confectionery and jam) absorb available moisture in food so that bacteria cannot multiply easily.

Warmth

Most food poisoning bacteria and fungi multiply at between 5°C and 63°C. This range of temperatures is therefore called the *danger zone*. (There's more information about the danger zone in Chapter 7.)

Ambient temperatures (room temperatures) are generally within the danger zone, and the ideal temperature for bacterial multiplication is about 37°C, which is the average human body temperature.

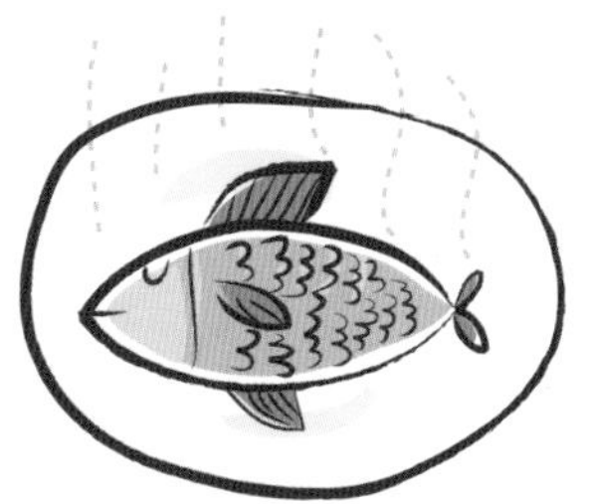

At temperatures colder than 5°C most bacterial multiplication slows down or stops altogether. This is why refrigerators should be at 5°C or cooler. Even so, most bacteria can survive cool temperatures and resume multiplication later when conditions are more suitable.

It is most important to note that some bacteria, such as *Listeria*, and some types of mould can carry on multiplying even when a refrigerator or chiller cabinet is operating at 5°C or cooler.

Freezing makes most bacteria dormant (inactive), but it may not kill them. When the frozen food is thawed any surviving bacteria can start multiplying at danger zone temperatures.

Cooking at high temperatures kills most bacteria, provided that the food is cooked for long enough. As a guide, food needs at least two minutes at 70°C right through to the centre or the thickest part of the product. However, some types of bacteria can survive by forming spores (see below). The toxins (poisons) produced by some bacteria and moulds can also survive ordinary cooking (*see* page 89).

Spores

Some types of bacteria form spores – a kind of protective coating – to survive high cooking temperatures and other harsh conditions, such as dehydration and disinfection. Bacteria do not multiply when they are in spore form but as soon as conditions improve, the bacteria emerge from their spores and are free to resume multiplication. Bacteria that form spores include *Bacillus cereus*, *Clostridium perfringens* and *Clostridium botulinum*.

Time

Bacteria need time in the right conditions to be able to multiply. When they have moist food and a warm temperature they need only about 10 to 20 minutes to do so. One bacterium splits in two, then two become four and four become eight, and so on. It does not take long for there to be enough pathogenic bacteria to cause food poisoning.

Key points

- For bacteria to multiply to levels that cause food poisoning, they need food, moisture, warmth and time.
- High-risk foods need special care to prevent causing food poisoning. In particular, they need to be kept out of the danger zone.
- Food is likely to be in the danger zone (5°C to 63°C) if it is left at an ambient temperature.
- Food passes through the danger zone while it is being cooled, thawed or heated.

Other bacterial requirements

Levels of acidity can affect multiplication. Vinegar has traditionally been used to preserve food by pickling. The presence, or lack, of oxygen also affects multiplication. Some bacteria, referred to as 'aerobes', need oxygen to multiply. Others, referred to as 'anaerobes', thrive without oxygen. This means that some bacteria can go on multiplying in unrefridgerated vacuum-packed foods, for example. There are also some bacteria that can live either with or without oxygen.

Handling high-risk foods

All food should be handled with care. When dealing with high-risk food, it is particularly important to:

- avoid touching the food by hand – use utensils whenever possible – to prevent cross-contamination
- keep raw and high-risk foods apart – raw foods are major sources of food poisoning bacteria
- cover the food during storage – to prevent contamination
- keep the food outside the danger zone temperatures of 5°C to 63°C whenever possible during preparation, service or sale – to prevent bacterial multiplication to levels that cause food poisoning.

Keep food covered during storage

Food passes through the danger zone while it is being heated

Key points

The basic rules for handling high-risk foods are to:

- prevent cross-contamination
- keep high-risk foods out of the danger zone whenever possible
- keep cold food really cold, ideally at 5°C or cooler
- keep hot food really hot, at 63°C or hotter.

Summary

1. High-risk foods are ready-to-eat foods. They are moist and protein-rich, providing the ideal conditions for the multiplication of pathogens to the levels that cause food poisoning when the food spends enough time in warm conditions.

2. For bacteria to multiply to levels that cause food poisoning, they need food, moisture, warmth and time.

3. High-risk foods need special care to prevent causing food poisoning. In particular, they need to be kept out of the danger zone.

4. Food is likely to be in the danger zone (5°C to 63°C) if it is left at an ambient temperature.

5. Food passes through the danger zone while it is being cooled, thawed or heated.

6. The basic rules for handling high-risk foods are to:

- prevent cross-contamination
- keep high-risk foods out of the danger zone whenever possible
- keep cold food really cold, ideally at 5°C or cooler
- keep hot food really hot, at 63°C or hotter.

Chapter 7
Time and temperature control

The best way to avoid causing illnesses from food is to prevent contamination. The problem is that bacteria and other micro-organisms are an essential part of the natural world, so many foods and ingredients are already contaminated when they arrive at your workplace. You must also therefore do everything possible to *control* the conditions that enable bacteria to multiply to the levels that cause food poisoning. You must also take every possible step to *destroy* pathogenic micro-organisms before food is eaten. This chapter deals with the principles involved.

Key words

Core temperature – the temperature at the centre or the thickest part of food.

Pasteurization – a form of heat treatment that kills pathogenic bacteria but not all spoilage bacteria.

Perishable – food that is likely to spoil (go bad) rapidly.

Time and temperature control – any measure necessary to keep food at a safe temperature or to destroy pathogenic micro-organisms.

Taking control

As you know, pathogenic bacteria need suitable food and moisture, plus warmth and time to multiply. They multiply rapidly on high-risk foods when they spend time in the danger zone – temperatures between 5°C and 63°C. As a consequence careful time and temperature control are needed to prevent causing food poisoning. The control involves three main types of action:

- restricting the time that high-risk foods are left at temperatures inside the danger zone – the rule of thumb is no more than four hours
- using low temperatures outside the danger zone to restrict bacterial multiplication – by freezing high-risk food, for example
- using high temperatures outside the danger zone to destroy pathogenic micro-organisms – by cooking food thoroughly, for example.

This means that the everyday basic rules of good practice are:

- keep high-risk foods out of the danger zone whenever possible
- keep cold food really cold – ideally at 5°C or cooler
- keep hot food really hot – at 63°C or hotter.

Key point

- Food poisoning bacteria multiply at temperatures between 5°C to 63°C, the temperature range known as the danger zone.

Recognising the danger times

It is not possible for foods to avoid the danger zone altogether, so it is important to be aware of when foods could be at a danger zone temperature. Such times include when food is:

- left standing in a room (at an ambient temperature)
- left in sunlight, for instance in a shop window
- being delivered and stored
- heated slowly
- cooled slowly.

Food is also likely to be in the danger zone when hot and cooler foods are combined – for instance, when a hot sauce is poured onto cold food, or hot foods are 'topped up'. This is why these practices are discouraged.

A high-risk food could pass through the danger zone several times before it is eaten. This could happen when, for instance, a frozen food is thawed, cooked, then cooled for serving cold later.

Whenever food spends time at a temperature in the danger zone bacteria have the chance to multiply rapidly.

The temperature of food left in direct sunlight can enter the danger zone

Poor practice

Many cases of food poisoning are linked to 'temperature abuse', when a high-risk food is kept in the danger zone for an unsafe period. The problems are usually caused by:

- cooling food too slowly before refrigeration
- preparing food too far ahead of sale or service and keeping it at ambient temperatures
- leaving food at ambient temperatures instead of refrigerating it
- reheating food inadequately
- under-cooking meat and poultry
- thawing frozen food insufficiently before cooking it
- holding hot food at a temperature below 63°C for periods that allow bacteria to multiply to unsafe levels.

Key point

- High-risk food may pass through the danger zone several times before it is consumed, so it is essential to limit the time that it spends at these temperatures.

Don't leave food in ambient temperatures

Low temperatures

Low temperatures outside the danger zone restrict the multiplication of most pathogens – but remember *Listeria* (*see* page 33). Refrigeration slows down bacterial activity, while freezing makes most bacteria dormant. Even so, refrigeration and freezing do not kill most bacteria and some parasites can survive freezing for quite long periods. There is more information about low temperatures in Chapter 12.

Low temperatures restrict the multiplication of most pathogens

Key point

- Refrigeration may slow down bacterial activity, but bacteria can still survive low temperatures.

High temperatures

High temperatures outside the danger zone can be used to destroy pathogenic micro-organisms in food. Cooking at 70°C or hotter for sufficient time kills most pathogenic bacteria, provided that the food is cooked thoroughly, right through to the core – the centre or the thickest part. Even so, some bacterial spores and some toxins survive ordinary cooking. As a consequence, some high-temperature processes, such as the pasteurization of milk, are used to make food safer, while others, such as commercial sterilization and ultra heat treatment (UHT), also help to prolong shelf life. There is more information about high temperatures in Chapters 12 and 13.

Cooking at 70°C or above will kill most pathogenic bacteria

High temperature processes – such as pasteurization – are used to make food safer

Key point

- High temperatures can be used to destroy pathogenic micro-organisms in food.

How to keep food out of the danger zone

The longer that a high-risk food is at a danger zone temperature, the more chances bacteria have to multiply to levels that cause food poisoning. So you and your colleagues need to control time and temperature at every stage. Examples of control include:

- ensuring that food is at a safe temperature when it is delivered to your workplace
- refrigerating raw, highly perishable and high-risk foods immediately after delivery
- keeping refrigerated food in storage until just before it is needed for preparation or serving
- cooking food thoroughly (see chart opposite)
- serving hot food at 63°C or hotter
- cooling food as rapidly as possible so that the food spends as short a time as possible at danger zone temperatures
- thawing frozen food by an approved method (*see* page 86), so that the outside of the food cannot reach danger zone temperatures while the inside is still frozen
- reheating food adequately, if it really must be reheated, to kill most pathogenic micro-organisms.

Key points

- Effective time and temperature control helps to prevent food poisoning by limiting the chances that pathogenic bacteria have to multiply.
- Low and high temperatures outside the danger zone can be used to restrict microbial multiplication and destroy the microbes that cause illness.
- The general rules for time and temperature control are to:
  - keep high-risk foods out of the danger zone whenever possible
  - keep cold food really cold: ideally at 5°C or cooler
  - keep hot food really hot: at 63°C or hotter.

Recommended safe temperatures

Stage of food handling	When to check temperature	Recommended safe temperatures
Delivery	Every time perishable food is delivered	0°C to 5°C is ideal for refrigerated food -22°C to -18°C is ideal for frozen food
Storage Refrigerator or cold store	Daily, at least	0°C to 5°C is ideal (the law in England, Wales and Northern Ireland permits up to 8°C)
Refrigerated storage counter or display	Daily, at least	0°C to 5°C is ideal (the law in England, Wales and Northern Ireland permits up to 8°C)
Deep freezer	Daily, at least	-18°C or below
Thawing frozen meat and poultry	Whenever food is thawed	0°C to 5°C
Cooking eg. joints of meat and poultry	Whenever food is cooked	*Minimum* core temperature of 70°C for 2 minutes
Cooling	Whenever food is cooled	10°C or cooler (ideally 5°C or cooler), ideally within 90 minutes
Reheating	Whenever food is reheated	*Minimum* recommended core temperature of 70°C for 2 minutes in England, Wales and Northern Ireland In Scotland there is a legal requirement to reheat food to a minimum of 82°C
Hot holding	Frequently throughout the holding period	*Minimum* core temperature of 63°C
Cold holding	Frequently throughout the holding period	0°C to 5°C is recommended

The chart above gives the temperatures that are generally accepted as good practice, together with the recommended period of time involved where appropriate. Keeping food at these temperatures plays a major part in ensuring that food is safe to eat.

However, different companies set slightly different rules for food temperatures, depending on the foods and processes involved, so it is important to check and to follow the rules covering your own work activities.

Measuring temperatures

Every company that handles food must check the temperature of food throughout the food flow – delivery, storage, preparation or processing, holding and sale – and should record the readings. This is to help to ensure that food stays outside the danger zone and to work within the law. If it is your job to check a temperature, you must be:

- trained how to check the temperature
- trained how to record the temperature
- informed which temperatures are unsafe
- instructed what to do if a reading is unsafe.

Devices

There is a range of temperature-measuring devices. They include scanners, probe thermometers and integrated equipment such as in refrigerators. Some integrated thermometers can be monitored and recorded automatically. The temperature may be given on a thermometer as a numerical scale on a dial, printed record or digital display.

Probe thermometers are just one type of temperature-measuring device

Calibration

Calibration is the process of checking and adjusting equipment so that it measures accurately. Some devices are calibrated by specialist contractors or the manufacturer. All devices must be calibrated according to the manufacturer's instructions:

- before they are first used
- at regular intervals, as a matter of course
- when there is damage to a device or an inaccurate reading is suspected
- according to your supervisor's instructions.

If it is your job to calibrate devices, you must be given appropriate training.

There are three main ways of calibrating a probe thermometer – by comparing it against a reference thermometer that is confirmed to be accurate, by the ice method or the boiling point method.

The ice method involves inserting the probe part of the device into a small container of crushed ice topped up with cold water. When the indicator has stabilised, the calibration nut may be turned until the indicator shows 0°C.

The boiling point method involves inserting the probe part of the thermometer into boiling water and, once the indicator has stabilised, adjusting it to show 100°C (at normal altitude).

Using thermometers

To avoid contamination and cross-contamination thermometers must be undamaged and must have been thoroughly cleaned and disinfected by an approved method before they are used.

When to measure temperatures

You should check temperatures according to your company's instructions. The chart on page 41 indicates typical times, such as when food is delivered, during storage and cooking. The temperature of high-risk foods being cooked or reheated should be measured towards the end of the predicted cooking period.

The temperature of frozen foods being thawed should be measured towards the end of the estimated thawing period. When hot holding, cold holding or cooling high-risk food, the temperature should be measured frequently. Refrigeration and freezer units should be checked at least once a day, more often if the unit doors are opened and closed frequently.

When measuring the temperature of food using a device, always follow the manufacturer's instructions

How to measure and record temperatures

Always follow the manufacturer's instructions, making sure to wait long enough for the reading to be accurate. It is important to measure the core temperature of any solid high-risk food that is under refrigeration or being cooked, reheated, cooled or thawed.

This can be done by inserting a clean, disinfected probe into the centre or the thickest part of the food. Cooked liquid food, such as soups, stews and sauces made from high-risk ingredients, should be stirred before the temperature is measured to ensure that the temperature is even throughout.

Probing refrigerated food can contaminate the food. If refrigerated food is used for testing the temperature, it must be thrown away once it has been probed. It is better practice to probe a special product substitute, or a container of covered water, that have been stored in the refrigerator for the purpose.

Alternative methods, depending on the measuring device, include hanging the probe – for example, in a freezer unit – or inserting the probe *between* packs of food, making sure that it is in close contact with the outer packaging.

Ensure that that you make a clear and careful note of the temperature in the manner and place that you have been instructed – the temperature log book, for instance.

TEMPERATURE LOG BOOK

Process step	Temperature	Monitoring method
Purchase, delivery/receipt		
Storage		
Preparation		
Cooking		
Hot holding		
Cooling		
Reheating		
Service and delivery to customers		

Corrective action

If a temperature reading is outside the acceptable range specified by your company, follow the correct procedure in your workplace for adjusting the temperature, reporting the problem, disposing of food and so on.

Key points

- Every company that handles food must check the temperature of food throughout the food flow and should record the readings.
- If it is your job to check a temperature, you must be:
  - trained how to check the temperature
  - trained how to record the temperature
  - informed which temperatures are unsafe
  - instructed what to do if a reading is unsafe.
- There is a range of temperature-measuring devices. They include scanners, probe thermometers and integrated equipment such as in refrigerators.
- Always follow the manufacturer's instructions, making sure to wait long enough for the reading to be accurate.
- Make a clear and careful note of the temperature in the manner and place that you have been instructed.

Summary

1. Food poisoning bacteria multiply at temperatures between 5°C to 63°C, the temperature range known as the danger zone.

2. High-risk food may pass through the danger zone several times before it is consumed, so it is essential to limit the time that it spends at these temperatures.

3. Refrigeration may slow down bacterial activity, but bacteria can still survive low temperatures.

4. High temperatures can be used to destroy pathogenic micro-organisms in food.

5. Effective time and temperature control helps to prevent food poisoning by limiting the chances that pathogenic bacteria have to multiply.

6. Low and high temperatures outside the danger zone can be used to restrict microbial multiplication and destroy the microbes that cause illness.

7. The general rules for time and temperature control are to:

   - keep high-risk foods out of the danger zone whenever possible
   - keep cold food really cold: ideally at 5°C or cooler
   - keep hot food really hot: at 63°C or hotter.

8. Every company that handles food must check the temperature of food throughout the food flow and should record the readings.

9. If it is your job to check a temperature, you must be:

- trained how to check the temperature
- trained how to record the temperature
- informed which temperatures are unsafe
- instructed what to do if a reading is unsafe.

10. There is a range of temperature-measuring devices. They include scanners, probe thermometers and integrated equipment such as in refrigerators.

11. Always follow the manufacturer's instructions, making sure to wait long enough for the reading to be accurate.

12. Make a clear and careful note of the temperature in the manner and place that you have been instructed.

Chapter 8
Personal hygiene

People are a common source of pathogenic bacteria, so everyone who works with food must have the highest possible standards of personal hygiene and personal habits to avoid contaminating food and causing illness.

Key words

Taint – alter the smell or taste of food.

Carrier – a person who carries pathogenic bacteria without suffering any symptoms of illness.

First impressions

It is good practice to start work clean and tidy every day. This will help you to feel good, give a favourable impression to any customers you meet and help to protect food from contamination. It helps to take a bath or shower every day. This will remove some of the bacteria that are naturally present on hair and skin, including those that thrive on stale perspiration and cause body odour. Using a deodorant can help to prevent unpleasant body smells from developing after you have washed, but you should avoid strongly scented deodorants, perfumes, aftershaves and other toiletries or cosmetics because they can taint some food.

Key point

- Keep yourself clean and tidy when working with food.

Essential hand hygiene

Even perfectly healthy people have potentially harmful microbes living on and in their bodies. These organisms can easily be transferred from your hands to food and cause illness.

There are many things you can do to avoid touching food with your bare hands – by using tongs or wearing disposable gloves, for example. Even so, you will touch equipment, utensils and surfaces as you work. To avoid causing contamination, you must ensure that your hands are scrupulously clean at all times. Handwashing helps to:

- remove pathogens (such as bacteria and viruses) and other harmful substances (such as dirt) from hands
- prevent direct food contamination and cross-contamination by your hands.

When to wash your hands

Always wash your hands:

before

- starting work
- touching raw food or high-risk food during any work with food

during any work with food

- as often as necessary to keep your hands clean
- when switching between handling raw and cooked food

after

- handling raw food
- visiting the toilet
- handling raw eggs in their shell
- coughing or sneezing into your hands or a handkerchief
- touching your hair or face
- carrying out cleaning jobs or touching containers of cleaning chemicals
- dealing with rubbish/waste and bins
- eating, drinking or smoking (in an area set aside for these activities).

How to wash your hands

It seems obvious how you should wash your hands, but research indicates that most people do not do so properly.

- Always use a hand basin provided exclusively for this purpose. (Never use a sink designed for food washing or washing up.)
- Use comfortably hot water and soap. Liquid soap is best because a bar of soap may carry bacteria left by the last person who used it.
- Work the soap into your hands by rubbing them together vigorously. This helps to remove bacteria. It is suggested that you take 15 to 20 seconds on this. Don't forget the areas between your fingers and around your wrists. It is advisable to use a nail brush to clean your nails after handling raw foods or going to the toilet.
- Rinse your hands before drying them. There are several methods available for drying your hands including disposable paper towels and clean roller towels. Never dry your hands on a tea towel or service cloth, your hands could contaminate them.

Key points

- Hands are a significant source of food contamination.
- To avoid causing contamination, you must ensure that your hands are scrupulously clean at all times.
- Wash your hands regularly throughout the work period. Always wash your hands when they are likely to be contaminated – for instance after going to the toilet or handling raw meat or poultry.

Always use a hand basin provided exclusively for washing hands

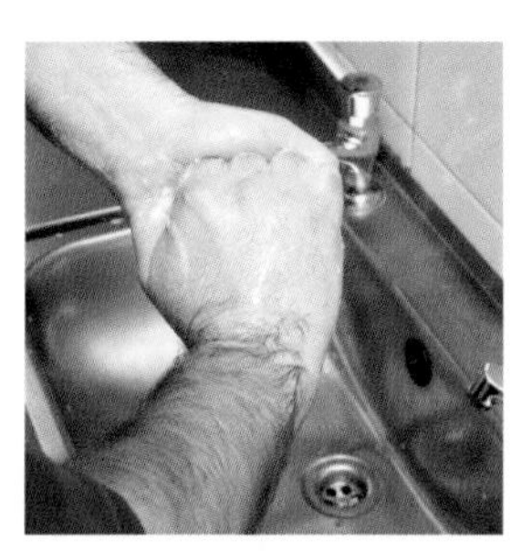

Use comfortably hot water, rub your hands vigorously to work in the soap

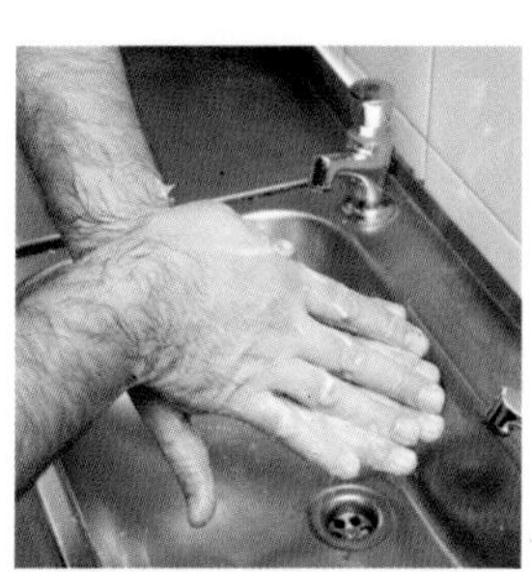

Don't forget the areas between your fingers and around your wrists

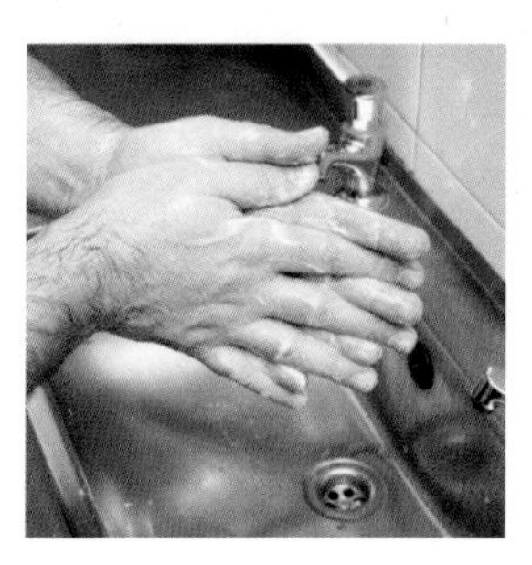

Rinse your hands before drying them

Nail polish

Do not wear nail varnish because it can chip and flake into food. It can also hide dirt that must be removed before handling food.

Cuts and spots

People are the main source of *Staphylococcus aureus* food poisoning bacteria that can be found on healthy people and in many cuts, spots and other skin conditions. To prevent spreading bacteria to food and to protect the wound or spot, always cover the affected area with a waterproof plaster. If the plaster is on your hands, you may need to wear gloves as well. Waterproof plasters should be brightly coloured – they are usually blue – so that they can be seen easily if they come off and appropriate action taken. Some plasters contain a thin metal strip so that they can be automatically identified by a metal detector on production lines. If a plaster does fall into food, tell your supervisor immediately.

If you have a septic cut or weeping spot or boil, you must report this to your supervisor *before* you start work (*see* page 52).

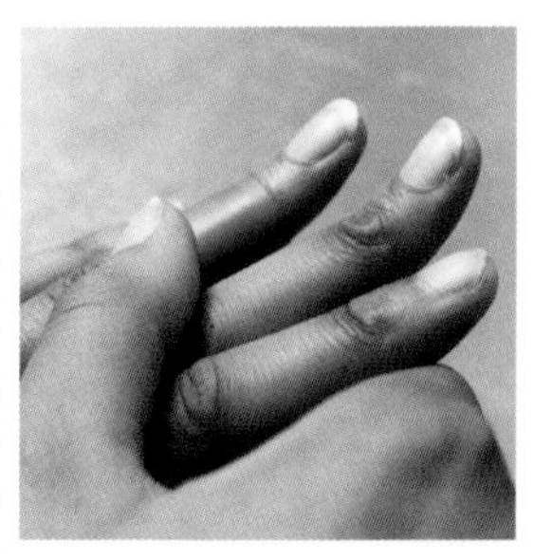

To prevent spreading bacteria to food always cover wounds or spots with a brightly-coloured, waterproof plaster

Key points

- Cuts, spots and some other skin conditions may have *Staphylococcus aureus* bacteria in them that can cause food poisoning.
- Cover spots and wounds with brightly-coloured plasters.

Appropriate clothes

What you need to wear depends upon the type of work you do. Typical examples include:

- overalls, jackets, trousers, aprons
- neck scarves, hats, hair nets, beard nets, moustache nets
- non-slip shoes, boots, safety shoes
- gloves, gauntlets.

Other clothes, such as body warmers, may also be provided for working in cold environments.

Although protective clothing may keep your own clothes clean, this is not their main purpose. Protective clothing is designed to protect food from contamination and you from harm. It should be:

- suitable for the work you do
- clean and in good condition
- light coloured, so that dirt will show easily, prompting you to change into clean replacement clothing
- easy to clean.

Always put on protective clothing *before* you go in to a food area to reduce the risk of contaminating food. Do not wear protective clothing outside food areas, such as on your way to work, because you could bring contaminants in to the food areas.

Hats

You need to wear a hat or head covering for many jobs involving food. It should cover as much of your hair as possible. In some companies food handlers must also wear hairnets to contain hair.

If your hair is long, it must be tied or clipped back so it cannot hang loose outside the head covering. Beards and moustaches should also be covered. Never brush or comb your hair in a food area otherwise you could contaminate food. Make sure that you put on the hat or head covering *before* you put on other protective clothing to avoid displacing hair.

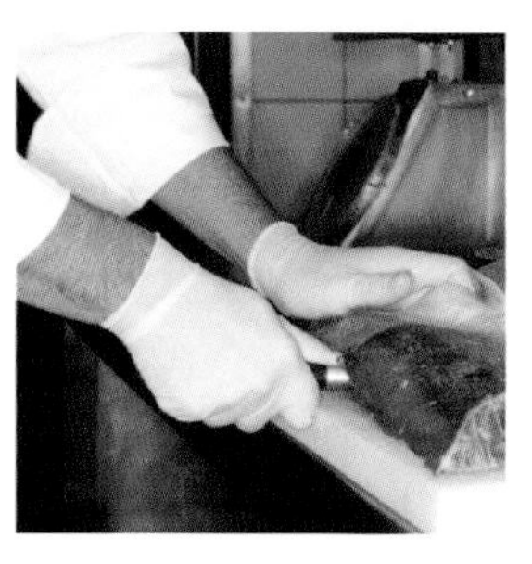

Depending on the type of work you do, you may be required to wear aprons, gloves or gauntlets

Outdoor clothing

Never wear or carry outdoor clothing, such as coats or jackets, into a food area because they could contaminate food or surfaces. Store outdoor clothes away from food areas: your employer should provide a separate area or locker for the purpose.

Jewellery

Leave jewellery, including watches, at home or in your locker at work. This is because bacteria can live on and under straps and rings, while gemstones and small parts could drop into food.

Some companies allow food handlers to wear a plain wedding ring and sleeper earrings, but they may have to be covered by a plaster. Find out the policy at your workplace.

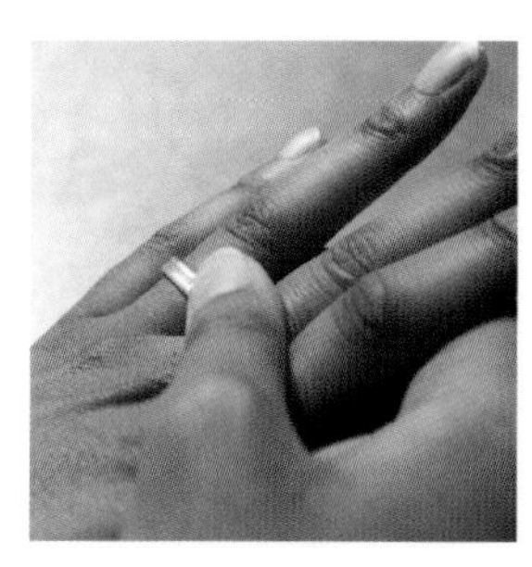

Bacteria can live on and under rings – so remove them or cover them with a plaster when at work

Key points

- Put on protective clothing before entering a food area.
- Keep your hair covered.

Unhygienic habits

Unhygienic habits can appear harmless until you remember how easily pathogens are spread. You must:

- never handle food without first washing your hands
- never forget to wash your hands after going to the toilet or dealing with rubbish
- never dry your hands on your clothing or on cleaning cloths such as wiping, drying or service cloths
- never pick your nose, or wipe your nose on a sleeve
- never cough or sneeze over food
- never spit
- never blow or breathe on glassware or cutlery to help polish them
- never use your fingers to test food, or a spoon that has not been washed thoroughly between each tasting
- never lick your finger tip to make it easier to pick up something or to separate flimsy materials such as paper or food wrap
- never eat or smoke in food areas, including behind a bar because you could drop ash or butts in the food, or transfer bacteria from your mouth to food.

Reporting illness

You must tell your employer (manager or supervisor or other designated person, such as a company nurse) if you have had, or are currently suffering from, food poisoning or any illness with similar symptoms. This is because:

- you must not work with food if you have certain illnesses or symptoms – because you could contaminate food
- it is a legal requirement to report certain illnesses to the health authorities – your employer should arrange for this to be done
- you may need medical attention
- you may need a doctor's approval before you can re-start work with food.

These are the symptoms you must tell your employer about:

- diarrhoea
- vomiting
- nausea
- ear, eye and nose discharges
- a septic cut, wound or other skin condition that leaves an open wound or broken skin, or any other skin condition or infection.

Report food-related illness before turning up for work

You must also report symptoms of food poisoning among members of your family or close personal contacts. This is because you could be a *carrier* – someone who carries pathogenic organisms, such as bacteria and viruses, without having any symptoms of the illness they cause. Carriers can unknowingly contaminate food or other people without becoming ill themselves.

If you have been ill with any of the symptoms listed opposite during a holiday abroad, you must tell your employer before you return to work. Your employer will tell you what to do. If you are told to see a doctor, you must tell the doctor that you are a food handler. Your doctor will decide whether any medical tests are needed. The doctor or your employer will also tell you when you can return to work.

Key points

- You must tell your employer about certain illnesses and symptoms before you work with food.
- You must report symptoms of food poisoning, discharges from your ears, eyes or nose and septic skin conditions.

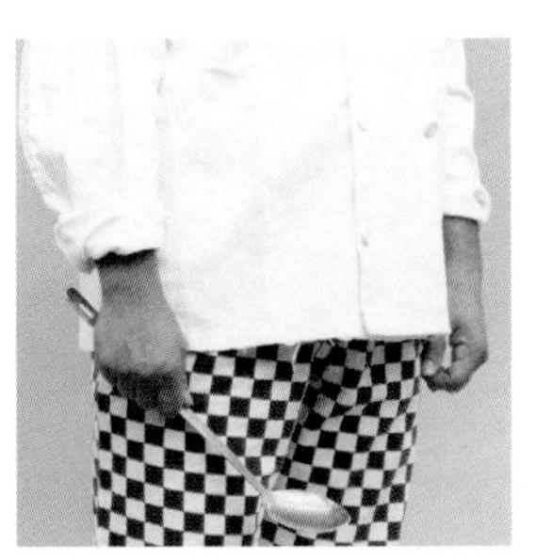

Keep yourself clean and tidy

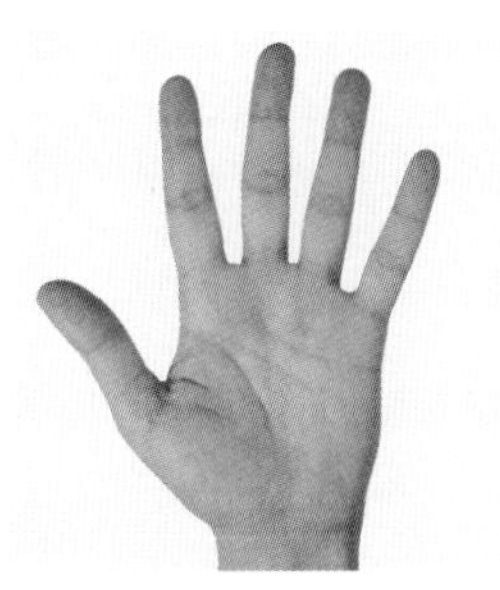

Make sure your hands are clean at all times

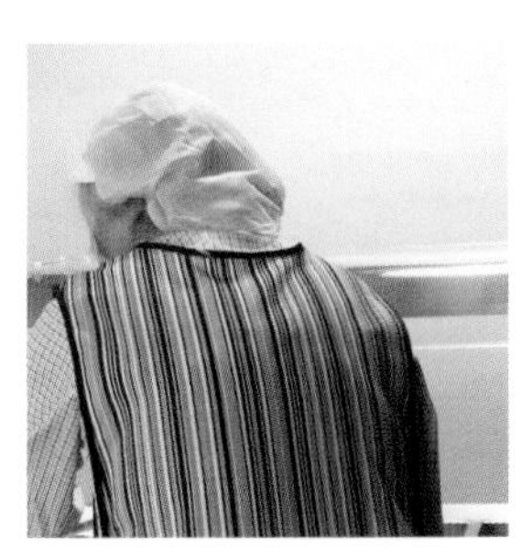

Put on protective clothing before entering a food area

Summary

1. Keep yourself clean and tidy when working with food.

2. Hands are a significant source of food contamination.

3. To avoid causing contamination, you must ensure that your hands are scrupulously clean at all times.

4. Wash your hands regularly throughout the work period. Always wash your hands when they are likely to be contaminated – for instance after going to the toilet or handling raw meat or poultry.

5. Cuts, spots and some other skin conditions may have *Staphylococcus aureus* bacteria in them that cause food poisoning.

6. Cover spots and wounds with brightly-coloured plasters.

7. Put on protective clothing before entering a food area.

8. Keep your hair covered.

9. You must tell your employer about certain illnesses and symptoms before you work with food.

10. You must report symptoms of food poisoning, discharges from your ears, eyes or nose and septic skin conditions.

Chapter 9
Premises and equipment

The construction, organisation and equipping of food premises all help to keep food safe. Although you may not have any responsibility for the way your workplace is organised, you do need to be aware of the general principles involved and the part you play in workflow and looking after food areas, utensils and equipment.

Key words

Durable – hard wearing.

Food-contact surface – any surface that touches food and therefore creates a contamination risk.

Food premises – anywhere that food is handled, including factories, shops, restaurants, market stalls, delivery vehicles, ships and aircraft.

Harbour – provide a shelter or hiding place.

Impervious – a material that does not let water through.

Non-porous – a material that does not allow liquids to penetrate.

Workflow – the route through food premises for food, food handlers and equipment during all the stages from delivery of raw food and ingredients to dispatch, sale or service of finished products.

Suitable for their use

Food premises must be suitable for the type of food used and the preparation and processes being carried out. The design, construction and equipping of food premises must minimise the risks from food hazards. This leads to a great variety in design, but there are some important general principles.

For example, food premises must:

- reduce the risk of food contamination
- enable staff to control the temperature of food
- enable staff to ventilate the premises adequately
- provide clean water
- provide facilities for personal hygiene and first aid
- provide enough suitable food storage and separate storage for other materials
- enable staff to clean thoroughly
- provide for the safe disposal of waste
- prevent pest infestation – for example, by door strip curtains, window screens or air curtains where appropriate
- create safe workflow (*see* page 56), particularly the separation of raw and ready-to-eat foods and the separation of clean and dirty activities.

Food premises should be designed, constructed and equipped to minimise the risks from food hazards

Key points

- The design of food premises should help staff to prevent contamination and to control food temperatures.
- Effective design of food premises enables raw and cooked food, as well as clean and dirty tasks, to be kept apart.
- The design of food premises should help to prevent pest infestation.
- The design, construction and equipping of food premises must minimise the risks from food hazards.

Workflow

Workflow is the route through food premises for food, food handlers and rubbish. It should safeguard food from contamination from the moment it is delivered until it is a finished product.

For example, storage areas should be near delivery areas and, wherever possible, deliveries should not be carried through food areas. Initial food preparation should take place as near the appropriate storage area as possible, with final work being carried out nearer to the area for packaging, sale or service. Food washing and washing up should take place as far away as possible from areas where food is ready to serve, sell or consume. Raw and ready-to-eat food should be kept apart.

Food handlers can play a part in safe workflow by planning their tasks so that they minimise the number of journeys around the food area.

Key points

- Workflow should safeguard food from contamination from the moment it is delivered until it is a finished product.
- There should be a well-planned route through the premises.
- Food handlers should plan their work to minimise journeys around the food area.

Construction

The surfaces of walls and ceilings must be smooth and without joints or cracks where bacteria or pests could harbour. Light-coloured materials are recommended so that dirt can be seen and removed quickly.

Walls, ceilings and floors must be grease resistant to prevent contamination. Coving between walls and floors makes cleaning easier and prevents food and insects from lying undetected.

Windows and doors should have screens or strip curtains where appropriate to reduce the risk of contamination. Woodwork must be smooth and sealed, without flaking paint.

The construction should also protect everyone's health and safety – for example, materials should be fire resistant where appropriate and floors should be non-slip.

Key point

- The best materials for the structure of food premises are durable, impervious, smooth and easy to clean.

Materials

The best materials for food equipment and utensils are:

- durable
- smooth and resistant to cracking or chipping
- easy to clean thoroughly
- non-porous
- non-toxic
- rust resistant.

All food-contact surfaces should be smooth, without cracks or joints, and heat resistant where appropriate. Tableware should be non-porous and without chips or cracks that could harbour bacteria. Colour-coded equipment and utensils are used in many companies to remind staff to separate preparation and processing involving raw and cooked food (*see* Chapter 4).

Key point

- Food equipment and utensils should be made from materials that are durable, impervious, smooth, resistant to cracking or chipping and easy to clean thoroughly.

Equipment

Equipment should be designed to provide easy access for cleaning. Large cookers, refrigerators and similar pieces of equipment should be mobile so they can be cleaned underneath.

There should be enough refrigerator space to store raw and cooked food apart. If there are not separate refrigerators or cold stores for segregated storage, extra care must be taken to store food safely.

All equipment and plant must be maintained and cleaned so that it does not cause physical contamination.

Equipment should be designed to provide easy access for cleaning

Durable, smooth, easy to clean, non-toxic and rust resistant

Key point

- The design of food premises, including the siting of equipment, should enable staff to clean easily and thoroughly.

Services and facilities

To help ensure food safety your employer must provide a number of facilities and services including good lighting and ventilation, hot water, toilets and basins for staff use. Basins for hand washing must be provided in the toilet area and there must also be at least one readily accessible hand wash basin in food preparation areas. Wash hand basins must be separate from any sinks for washing food or washing up.
All basins should have:

- hot and cold running water (ideally with foot-operated or wrist-operated taps to prevent cross-contamination)
- hand-washing materials, such as liquid soap
- drying materials, such as disposable or automatic linen towels.

Never attempt to wash food or utensils in a wash hand basin, and never wash your hands at a sink – you could spread bacteria.

Key point

- Never wash food or utensils in a wash hand basin, and never wash your hands at a sink – you could spread bacteria.

First aid

Your employer should also provide a properly stocked first aid box within easy reach. It should include brightly coloured waterproof plasters. First aid equipment is indicated by a white cross on a green background.

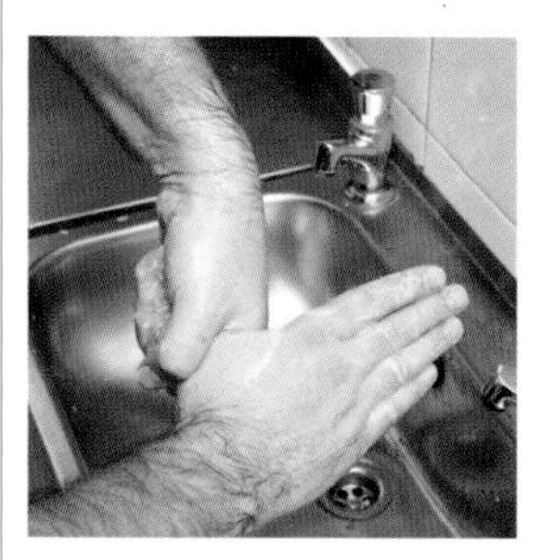

Wash hand basins must be separate from sinks for washing food or washing up

Summary

1. The design of food premises should help staff to prevent contamination and to control food temperatures.

2. Effective design of food premises enables raw and cooked food, as well as clean and dirty tasks, to be kept apart.

3. The design of food premises should help to prevent pest infestation.

4. The design, construction and equipping of food premises must minimise the risks from food hazards.

5. Workflow should safeguard food from contamination from the moment it is delivered until it is a finished product.

6. There should be a well-planned route through the premises.

7. Food handlers should plan their work to minimise journeys around the food area.

8. The best materials for the structure of food premises are durable, impervious, smooth and easy to clean.

9. Food equipment and utensils should be made from materials that are durable, impervious, smooth, resistant to cracking or chipping and easy to clean thoroughly.

10. The design of food premises, including the siting of equipment, should enable staff to clean easily and thoroughly.

11. Never wash food or utensils in a wash hand basin, and never wash your hands at a sink – you could spread bacteria.

Chapter 10
Cleaning and disinfection

Consumers expect food premises to be clean.This not only creates a good impression, but also helps to make a safe, pleasant environment for everyone. However, it is important to remember that even when something looks perfectly clean, it could be contaminated. This chapter outlines the principles involved in cleaning.

The aim of cleaning

Cleaning is the process of making something free from dirt and contamination. It involves the use of energy – *your* effort or that of a machine, such as a dishwasher or floor scrubber. Activities include wiping, rubbing, scrubbing, scouring, brushing and sweeping. Cleaning is intended to keep food and workplaces safe.

In particular, cleaning aims to:

- protect food from biological contamination
- reduce opportunities for bacterial multiplication, by removing food particles
- protect food from physical and chemical contamination
- avoid attracting pests
- maintain a safe environment, for example to stop someone from slipping on a greasy floor
- give consumers a good impression
- carry out legal and moral obligations to keep food safe.

Key point

- Cleaning is the process of making something free from dirt and contamination.

Key words

Clean – free from dirt and grease.

Clean as you go – cleaning procedures carried out as you work.

Cleaning schedule – a document that sets out the details of scheduled cleaning.

Contact time – the period when a disinfectant or sanitizer must remain on or around a surface to achieve disinfection.

Detergent – a chemical that helps to dissolve grease and remove dirt.

Disinfection – the process of reducing pathogenic micro-organisms to safe levels.

Disinfectant – a chemical that reduces pathogenic microbes to safe levels.

Sanitizer – a chemical that both cleans and disinfects.

Scheduled cleaning – cleaning carried out by specified people at specified intervals and times.

Sterilization – the process of killing all pathogenic micro-organisms.

Detergents

Detergents help to dissolve grease and remove dirt. The combination of the use of energy, a detergent and hot water will kill some pathogenic bacteria, but most will survive. To prevent the bacteria from causing illness, some items and equipment must also be disinfected after they have been cleaned.

Key point

- Detergents help to dissolve grease and remove dirt.

Disinfection

Disinfection is the reduction of bacteria to a low, safe level. It can be achieved by the use of:

- very hot water, at 82°C or hotter
- steam
- chemical disinfectants.

Heat disinfection and chemical disinfection are often combined.

Disinfectants

Chemicals that reduce pathogenic micro-organisms to a safe level are called disinfectants. They destroy enough bacteria to safeguard health, even though they cannot kill all pathogenic bacteria or any spores. Disinfectants must be used *after* cleaning, because they cannot remove the grease and dirt that stop them working properly. Disinfectants must be left on the surface for long enough to work properly: this is referred to as the contact time. The manufacturer's instructions should give details of the required contact time for each disinfectant.

Sanitizers

Sanitizers combine the work of a detergent and a disinfectant. They clean *and* disinfect, provided there is sufficient contact time. Many companies use a sanitizer instead of using a detergent followed by a disinfectant.

Key points

- Disinfectants reduce bacteria to a low, safe level.
- With sufficient contact time, sanitizers clean and disinfect.

What to disinfect

The items you disinfect depend to some extent upon their use and it is important to find out which items you need to disinfect. Surfaces that come into contact with raw or high-risk foods, anything that is frequently touched by hand and other items that create a serious risk of contamination or bacterial multiplication must be cleaned and disinfected or sanitized after every use and, where relevant, between use for different foods. In general, you need to disinfect/sanitize:

food-contact surfaces, including:

- chopping boards, preparation tables/work surfaces
- food processing machinery and plant, such as slicers, mixers and mincers, and knives, tongs and other utensils
- containers
- production belts

hand-contact surfaces, including:

- handles – doors, refrigerators, freezers, cupboards, drawers
- taps
- switches

contamination and bacterial multiplication hazards, such as:

- cloths and mops
- waste bins and their lids.

Key point

- Food-contact surfaces, hand-contact surfaces and anything that could cause contamination or provide the conditions for bacterial multiplication must be disinfected after cleaning.

You need to disinfect hand-contact and food-contact surfaces

When to clean

Clean as you go

Items and areas where there are likely to be pathogenic bacteria, such as chopping boards and production belts, must be cleaned and disinfected frequently throughout the work period. This is commonly described as clean-as-you-go cleaning. It involves clearing and cleaning up *immediately after* every task. For example, you should clean and disinfect work surfaces after handling raw meat. *You* are responsible for cleaning as you go.

Scheduled cleaning

Some equipment and areas may be cleaned at less frequent intervals than those that need to be cleaned as you go. For example, the interval could be daily (for a floor and bins), weekly (for underneath a refrigerator) and monthly or quarterly (for high-level cleaning).

Your employer is responsible for working out a timetable, known as a cleaning schedule, that sets out when and how different items and areas should be cleaned and who should do the cleaning. The cleaning schedule should show the:

- item or area to be cleaned
- frequency of cleaning required
- method, including the chemicals to use, the protective clothing to wear and the safety precautions to take
- staff involved, including the name of the person responsible for checking that the cleaning has been carried out effectively.

The cleaning schedule may also include the names of cleaning contractors who carry out specialist tasks, such as moving or dismantling machinery or using particularly hazardous chemicals or techniques.

Clean as you go

Key points

- Food handlers are responsible for clean-as-you-go cleaning. This involves clearing away and cleaning (and disinfecting where appropriate) immediately after every task.
- Your employer is responsible for working out a cleaning schedule, that sets out when and how different items and areas should be cleaned and who should do the cleaning.

Examples of cleaning

Cleaning a work surface

- Protect food from contamination before you start cleaning.
- Remove any loose dirt from the surface.
- Wash the surface with hot water and an appropriate detergent, using a cloth, brush or a scourer.
- Rinse with hot water and a clean cloth.
- Use a chemical disinfectant, following the manufacturer's instructions. Don't forget the contact time.
- Rinse with clean water.
- Allow to dry in the air (air dry) or use a disposable paper towel.

Washing up

Dishwashers provide an effective way to clean and disinfect items used in the preparation of food. Rinse cycles usually run at 82°C to 89°C. Always follow the manufacturer's instructions, making sure that the machine is stacked without blocking the cleaning jets and is filled with the right amount of the correct chemicals.

Washing by hand

Many food activities involve washing some items by hand. Wherever possible, use two sinks side by side.

- Wear rubber gloves to protect your hands from the hot water and chemicals.
- Remove particles of food – scrape and rinse if necessary.
- Wash the items, ideally in the first sink, with hot water (at about 55°C) and detergent, using a cloth, brush or scourer. Replace the water if it becomes cool or greasy.
- Rinse in very hot water – at 82°C is ideal – using a second sink if possible. Leave the items to soak for 30 seconds. If possible, use a purpose-designed basket to lower and lift the items out of the water.
- Dry the items, preferably by leaving them to air dry, in a clean, dry area safe from contamination.

Safety precautions

Before you start cleaning, make sure that food is stored safely out of the way and cannot be contaminated. If you are cleaning a refrigerator, cold room or freezer, ensure that the food is kept at a safe temperature outside the danger zone.

Switch off and isolate electrical equipment – such as slicers, refrigerators, vending machines, processing machines and production belts – with *dry* hands *before* you start to clean.

Work through the stages of cleaning (see opposite) in a way that does not spread dust or dirt. Avoid being distracted in a way that puts you, other people or food at risk. Always wash your hands before starting another task.

Using cleaning products safely

Ensure that you understand how to use a cleaning chemical safely and always follow the manufacturer's instructions. Wear protective clothing, such as rubber gloves and goggles, appropriate to the task. If you are in any doubt about the safe use of a chemical, ask your supervisor for advice before you start work. Use only the chemicals approved by your employer for the task. Never mix chemicals together – they could explode, cause toxic fumes or could 'burn' someone's skin.

Always store chemicals away from food in the labelled containers designed for that purpose.

Key point

- Food handlers must follow safety procedures when working with cleaning chemicals so that they protect food from contamination and people from injury.

The stages of wet cleaning and disinfecting

There are six main stages in most wet cleaning tasks. When a sanitizer is used, stages 2 to 4 are combined.

1. **Prepare** – remove loose and heavy soiling. For example, scrape plates and chopping boards, or soak a saucepan.

2. **Clean** – wash with hot water and detergent. (If using a sanitizer, leave it for the specified contact time, then move to stages 5 and 6.)

3. **Rinse** – remove any traces of detergent and food particles with clean, hot water.

4. **Disinfect** – use a chemical disinfectant, making sure to leave it on for the correct contact time.

5. **Final rinse** – use clean, hot water.

6. **Dry** – if possible, leave items to dry naturally in the air, because the use of drying cloths can spread bacteria. If you have to use a cloth, try to use disposable paper ones. Cloths made from fabric must be clean and dry. They must be replaced frequently and used for one batch of drying only.

Cleaning cloths and equipment

Dishcloths, wiping cloths, service cloths and tea-towels often become contaminated by bacteria and microscopic food particles. As a consequence, single-use disposable ones are recommended. If your workplace provides only re-usable cloths, such as tea-towels, make sure that you use clean ones. Replace used cloths with clean ones frequently. Some companies provide colour-coded cloths for use in specified areas (such as washing up) to help to prevent cross-contamination. Never use cloths in food areas that have previously been used for cleaning toilet areas, floors or drains. Never use service cloths or oven gloves for cleaning tasks or for drying your hands.

Clean and disinfect cloths and mops immediately after use and leave them to dry in the air. Do *not* leave them to soak in disinfectant for longer than the manufacturer's recommended contact time because bacteria may become resistant to the chemicals. Store cleaning equipment and protective clothing away from food.

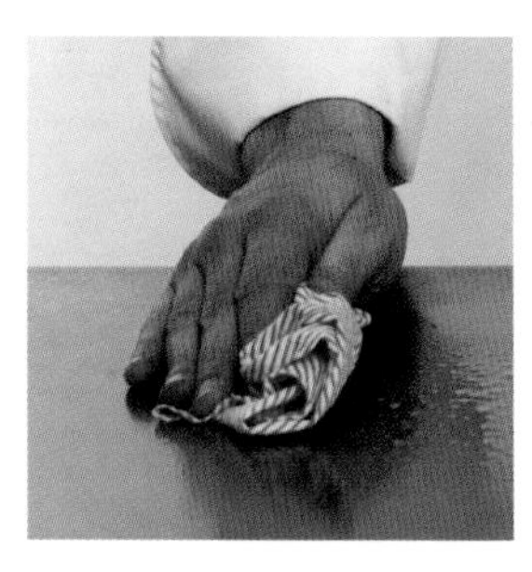

Single-use disposable cloths are recommended to prevent the risk of contamination

Key point

- Cloths often become contaminated with bacteria so, if possible, use single-use disposable ones.

Sterilization

Sterilization is the process of destroying all pathogens and spoilage organisms. It is not usually necessary or possible to sterilize food premises and equipment but medical equipment is routinely sterilized.

Key point

- Sterilization destroys all pathogens and spoilage organisms.

Rubbish disposal

Bins are needed near food preparation areas, but not so close that they cause contamination. They are also needed outside. A bin or bin stand indoors should have a well-fitting lid and be lined with a disposable polythene sack. Foot-operated bins are best because you do not have to touch any part of the bin by hand. Leave bin lids closed, unless you are throwing something away. Never let the container overflow or leave rubbish inside food premises overnight – it will attract pests. Tell your employer if bins become full: additional bins or collections may be needed.

Remove rubbish from indoors as soon as each bag becomes full. Tie the bag securely and take it outside to a refuse container with a tight-fitting lid to keep out scavengers, such as cats and foxes.

Keep bins, their lids and the area around them clean and tidy at all times. Always empty and clean indoor bins and their lids at the end of the work period.

Always wash your hands after handling refuse and waste food.

As soon as a rubbish bag is full, tie it securely and take it outside to the refuse container

Key points

- Rubbish bins indoors should be emptied regularly throughout the work period.
- Bin bags should not be left lying around outside because they could attract pests.

Summary

1. Cleaning is the process of making something free from dirt and contamination.

2. Detergents help to dissolve grease and remove dirt.

3. Disinfectants reduce bacteria to a low, safe level.

4. With sufficient contact time, sanitizers clean and disinfect.

5. Food-contact surfaces, hand-contact surfaces and anything that could cause contamination or provide the conditions for bacterial multiplication must be disinfected after cleaning.

6. Food handlers are responsible for clean-as-you-go cleaning. This involves clearing away and cleaning (and disinfecting where appropriate) immediately after every task.

7. Your employer is responsible for working out a cleaning schedule that sets out when and how different items and areas should be cleaned and who should do the cleaning.

8. Food handlers must follow safety procedures when working with cleaning chemicals so that they protect food from contamination and people from injury.

9. Cloths often become contaminated with bacteria so, if possible, use single-use disposable ones.

10. Sterilization destroys all pathogens and spoilage organisms.

11. Rubbish bins indoors should be emptied regularly throughout the work period.

12. Bin bags should not be left lying around outside because they could attract pests.

Chapter 11
Food pests

Pests can cause serious health and economic problems. They can contaminate food, spread disease, destroy food and damage premises. This chapter outlines your role in preventing a pest infestation.

Key words

Feral – wild.

Infestation – the presence of pests.

Pest – an animal or insect that contaminates or damages food.

Pet – tamed, domestic animal.

Typical pests

A food pest is any creature that lives on, or in, human food, causing damage or contamination or both. The main pests are:

- **insects** – such as flies, moths, ants, cockroaches and wasps
- **stored product pests** – such as beetles, mites and weevils
- **rodents** – rats and mice
- **birds** – mainly feral pigeons, sparrows, starlings and seagulls.

Pet animals in food areas can also contaminate food. There have been cases of food poisoning where someone has contaminated food after handling pets.

Key point

- A food pest is any creature that lives on, or in, human food, causing damage or contamination or both.

The attraction of food premises

Pests are attracted to places where food is stored, prepared, sold, served or thrown away, and to where there is warmth and shelter.

They can enter buildings through open windows and doors, or through the tiniest cracks in walls and around windows and pipes. Food premises are attractive to pests because they contain everything most pests need to survive:

- **food** – in storage, under preparation or as waste
- **moisture** – as condensation from cooking activities, from dripping taps or from stored liquids
- **warmth** – from heating systems or from handling and processing activities
- **shelter** – for sleeping or nesting in any undisturbed areas, such as under a refrigerator that has not been moved regularly for cleaning or the back of a store that has not been checked frequently.

Key point

- Food premises attract pests because they contain almost everything that pests need to survive.

Biological hazards

Many pests inhabit unhealthy places where they pick up pathogenic bacteria on their bodies and legs. For example, rats live in sewers, while flies feed and breed in rubbish tips, dustbins, drains and animal droppings. Some pests also have pathogenic bacteria living *inside* their bodies and these can be spread to food from their droppings or through their saliva as they eat. As well as spreading food poisoning bacteria, pests can spread food-borne illnesses, such as dysentery and illnesses such as Weil's disease (from water contaminated by rat urine).

Physical hazards

Pests are also a physical hazard. Their droppings, eggs, fur, nest material, mites, parasites and their own dead bodies can all cause contamination.

Pests can cause physical, as well as biological, contamination

Key point

- Pests are a source of biological and physical contamination.

Consequences of pest infestations

- The spread of diseases, including food poisoning and food-borne illness.
- Damage to the business's reputation and profit.
- Damage to buildings, equipment and electrical cables, causing fire and other safety hazards.
- Non-compliance with the law, possibly leading to court cases, fines and possible closure of the business.

Pests can spread disease and cause damage

Preventing problems

Your employer is responsible for ensuring that your workplace is designed and equipped to keep pests out and must take swift, safe measures to deal with any infestation that occurs. You play an important part in preventing problems by:

- keeping food covered at all times
- storing food off the floor in appropriate containers
- never leaving food outside
- checking deliveries carefully – pests can enter food premises in packaging, vegetables, fruit, cereals and grain
- checking stored goods regularly and rotating stock (*see* Chapter 12)
- reporting any damaged (torn, pierced or gnawed) packaging to your supervisor
- storing food waste in bins with securely fitting lids
- maintaining a clean workplace – paying special attention to food preparation areas, stores, drains, gullies and bin areas – and cleaning as you go, ensuring that you clear up any spilled food immediately
- keeping door and window screens closed
- telling your supervisor about any holes in brickwork or around windows, doors or pipes.

Prevention is always better than the cure but it is also important to watch out for signs of pests. Do so regularly and particularly during stock rotation, cleaning and dealing with refuse. Report any sightings of pests or signs of trouble to your supervisor immediately. The main signs are:

- dead bodies (mainly insects, rodents and birds)
- droppings
- unusual smells
- scratching, pecking or gnawing sounds (mainly rodents and birds)

- gnawed pipes, cables and fittings (mainly rodents)
- torn or damaged sacks or packaging, sometimes surrounded by spilled food
- eggs, larvae, pupae, feathers, fur, nesting material
- paw or claw prints
- smears and rat runs (rodents).

Key point

- Effective pest control includes preventing pests from getting into premises, protecting food from contamination and taking immediate action to deal with a suspected infestation.

Dealing with an infestation

Your supervisor will tell you what to do if there is an infestation. It may be dangerous to attempt to deal with a pest infestation unless you have been trained and given authority to do so. Most companies use a competent specialist contractor to kill pests. For your own safety and that of others, it is essential not to touch or interfere with anything designed to eliminate pests. Most infestations may be tackled using bait and baited traps; poisons – pesticides and insecticides; or electric ultraviolet fly killers.

Key points

- Food handlers should report sightings and signs of pests to their employer.
- It may be dangerous to interfere with any pest prevention measures or equipment.

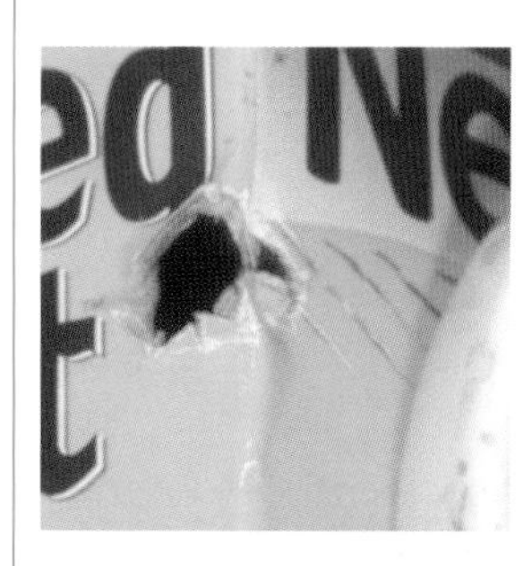

Watch out for signs of pests

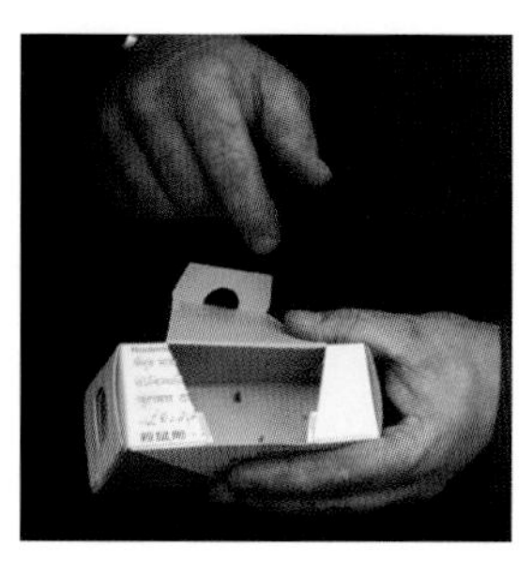

Don't interfere with pest prevention measures or equipment

Summary

1. A food pest is any creature that lives on, or in, human food, causing damage or contamination or both.

2. Food premises attract pests because they contain almost everything that pests need to survive.

3. Pests are a source of biological and physical contamination.

4. Effective pest control includes preventing pests from getting into premises, protecting food from contamination and taking immediate action to deal with a suspected infestation.

5. Food handlers should report sightings and signs of pests to their employer.

6. It may be dangerous to interfere with any pest prevention measures or equipment.

Chapter 12
From production to safe storage

Everyone wants their food to be delicious and safe to eat, so all products and ingredients need constant care from growing or producing, through transporting, storing and preparing right up to selling or serving. At every stage it is essential to handle and store food in the best possible way – in the right conditions, at the correct temperature and for a safe time. This chapter outlines the principles involved in keeping food safe and in best condition.

Key words

Date mark – a date on packaging indicating the period when the food is safe and in the best condition to eat. Date marks include *use-by* dates for highly perishable food and *best-before* dates for less perishable items.

Dehydration – the removal of moisture; drying.

Freezer burn – dehydration damage to food caused by ice crystals during freezing.

Perishable – foods that spoil (go bad) quickly.

Preservation – the safe treatment of food to delay spoilage.

Shelf life – the storage period when food is safe to eat and in the best condition.

Stored product pests – insects, such as weevils, beetles, moths and their larvae, that contaminate foods and ingredients, such as flour, cereals and nuts, kept in a dry goods store.

Use-by and best-before dates – dates on food packaging that indicate the period when the food is safe and in the best condition to eat. A *use-by* date is displayed on highly perishable food while a *best-before* date indicates a food item with a longer shelf life.

Natural factors

Even before food arrives at your workplace, a gradual process of ageing has begun. This natural process, known as spoilage, starts from the moment food is slaughtered, caught or harvested. It is caused mainly by the action of micro-organisms such as spoilage bacteria and fungi (mould and yeast).

The *speed* of spoilage can be controlled – by preservation methods and safe food handling practices – so that food is both acceptable to consumers and safe for eating. However, food spoilage may also be accelerated by, for example, rough handling, inappropriate storage conditions (especially poor temperature control) or contamination by pests or chemicals.

If you control the conditions that encourage *pathogenic* bacteria to multiply rapidly, you will also help to control the conditions that encourage *spoilage* bacteria to multiply. This means that you will be helping to:

- maintain the quality of food and keep it acceptable to consumers
- prevent illness
- carry out your legal responsibilities for food safety.

Key points

- Food handlers have legal responsibilities to do everything possible to keep food safe and it is illegal to sell spoilt food.
- Spoilage is the natural process of ageing, or deterioration, that makes food unacceptable to customers.
- Spoilage is caused by spoilage bacteria, mould and yeast.
- Spoilage can be accelerated by careless handling, inappropriate storage and pest infestation.

Protection for your supplies

The bacteria, moulds and yeasts that cause spoilage need food, moisture, warmth and time to reproduce. Preservation methods deprive the microbes of these ideal conditions for multiplication.

For thousands of years techniques, such as drying, salting and smoking, have been used to prolong the period when food is safe, appetising and nutritious to eat – what we now call the shelf life.

Modern preservation techniques have improved some old methods and created new ones. Some methods make food safer to eat (by destroying pathogens), as well as lengthening the shelf life. The main methods of preservation are:

- **heat treatment** – in cooking, canning, bottling, commercial sterilization, pasteurization and ultra heat treatment (UHT)
- **the use of low temperatures** – the freezing and refrigeration of a wide range of perishable foods
- **drying** (dehydration) – particularly of fish, meat, fruit, vegetables, soups, stocks and beverages
- **chemical preservation** – in processes including curing, salting and pickling
- **vacuum sealing/vacuum packing/sous vide/ controlled atmospheres** – used especially for meat, fish, poultry and some vegetables
- **smoking** – particularly for fish, meats (especially ham and sausages) and poultry
- **irradiation** – a method of preservation that kills spoilage and pathogenic microbes.

Once the packaging of most preserved food has been opened, the contents must usually be stored and handled as if they were fresh.

Key point

- Preservation techniques are used to prolong the period when food is safe, appetising and nutritious to eat.

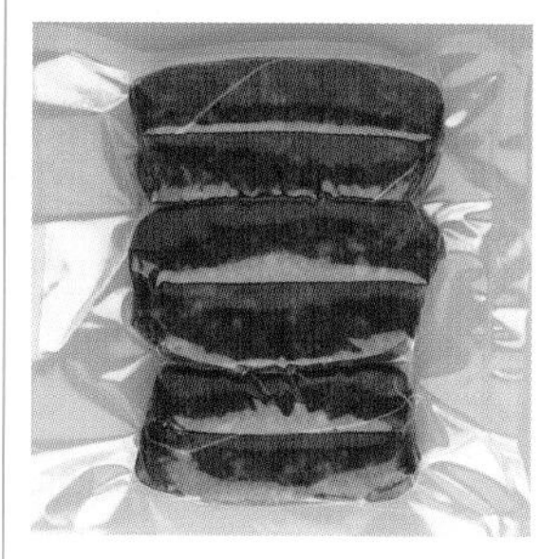

Preservation methods include drying, pickling and vacuum packing

Recognising spoilt food

Spoilt food is unacceptable to most customers and it is illegal to sell such food. (Remember that some of the conditions that accelerate spoilage, such as poor temperature control, also encourage food poisoning bacteria to multiply. So, spoilt food is often unsafe to eat.) It is therefore essential to be able to recognise the signs of spoilage. Typical indications include:

- discolouration, including dark or pale patches
- visible mould
- changes to the usual smell, often unpleasant
- changes in texture, including wrinkling and drying, softening and becoming pulpy
- alteration of the usual flavour, including sourness
- 'blown' cans of food – bulging caused by the action of spoilage micro-organisms.

It is essential to be able to regognise the signs of spoilage

Key point

- It is essential to be able to recognise the signs of spoilage.

Date marks

Even though food handlers must make careful checks on the appearance and smell of food, it is not possible to detect every possible problem caused by spoilage or pathogenic micro-organisms. As a consequence, there is a system of date marking that is based upon scientific research. There are two kinds of date mark that are legal requirements in the UK. They are:

- *use by*
- *best before*.

You may also come across date codes applied by individual companies to help to maintain quality and food safety. It is against the law to alter a date mark without re-treating or processing the food correctly.

Use by

Highly perishable packaged food, such as cooked meat, fish and dairy products, must by law be marked with a *use-by* date. Any food that has passed this date is likely to be unfit to eat and could cause illness. It is against the law to sell or serve food that has gone beyond a *use-by* date.

Best before

Less perishable items, such as frozen food, dried fruit, flour, biscuits, cereals and canned food, must carry a *best-before* date. This indicates when food is in its best condition.

Key point

- Highly perishable foods must be labelled with a *use-by* date mark, while products with a longer shelf life must have a *best-before* date mark.

Your role

Someone in your organisation has the responsibility for buying food from reputable suppliers and setting up systems that reduce the risks from food hazards. Your exact part in the flow of food from farm to fork depends upon your individual job, but you are likely to be generally responsible for:

- preventing contamination – for example, by keeping food covered and by separating raw and high-risk foods
- making visual checks on the condition of food
- checking code dates before using, serving or selling food
- keeping storage areas clean and disinfected
- reporting any signs of spoilage or possible food safety hazard to your supervisor.

The rest of this chapter outlines specific tasks that you may be asked to carry out.

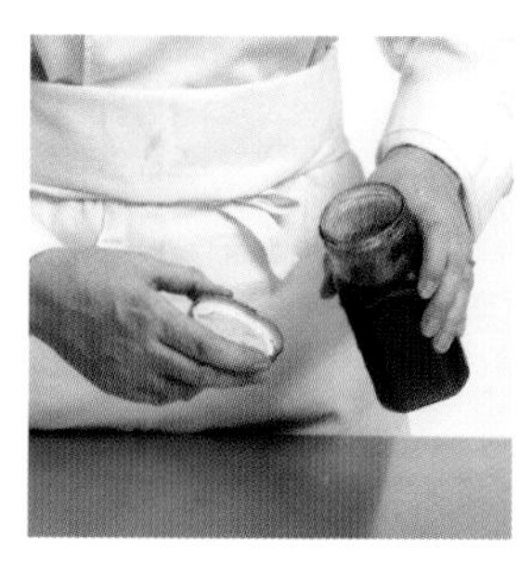

Check food for spoilage before use

Dealing with food deliveries

Someone is responsible for checking the condition of food delivery vehicles when they arrive at your workplace. Vehicles used for delivering food should be specifically designed for transporting food and must be kept clean. They should be refrigerated if they carry high-risk or highly perishable foods.

Deliveries must be checked as soon as they arrive and the food must be stored immediately afterwards.

Every food business should have guidelines for accepting or rejecting food deliveries. You need to check the details for different foods, but the key points are to ensure that the food is:

- fresh and within the date code
- at the correct temperature
- contained in clean, undamaged packaging
- free from pest infestation.

Reasons for rejecting a consignment on food include:

- high-risk or perishable foods delivered at a danger zone temperature
- frozen food thawed or partly thawed
- packaging damaged, dirty or wet
- cans dented, bulging, rusty or leaking
- signs of mould or other forms of spoilage
- an expired date mark, when food has gone past a *use-by* or *best-before* date
- inadequate documentation.

Key points

- Deliveries of food should be checked for condition, temperature and shelf life.
- Food should be stored immediately after checking a delivery. High-risk, perishable and frozen foods should be stored before other types of food because they need to stay out of the danger zone or remain frozen.

The aim of storage

Most food businesses have to store food, even if that storage period is brief. Correct storage helps to:

- prevent illness linked to food
- preserve the food's taste, appearance and nutritional value
- provide adequate supplies when they are needed
- avoid spoilage and wasted food
- keep to the budget
- keep within the law and avoid prosecution for selling unfit food.

Types of storage

Food stores should be designed to conserve different types of food in the best possible way. Typical storage areas include:

- **dry goods stores** – for short and long-term storage of, for example, canned and bottled food, cereals, grains, tea, coffee and spices
- **refrigerators and cold stores** – for storing high-risk and perishable foods for short periods
- **chiller cabinets and refrigerated vending machines** – for displaying food for very short periods
- **freezers** – for longer-term storage of frozen food.

There should also be separate storage for cleaning chemicals and equipment; protective clothing; and food handlers' outdoor clothing.

Dry goods store for short and long-term storage

Chiller cabinets are used for displaying food for short periods

General rules for safe storage

Different foods have different storage requirements but there are some important general rules.

- Keep storage areas clean and disinfected.
- Store food immediately after the delivery has been checked.
- Deal with high-risk, frozen and perishable foods before dry and canned goods.
- Keep high-risk and perishable foods out of the temperature danger zone.
- Separate high-risk and ready-to-eat foods.
- Handle everything with care: rough handling can accelerate spoilage.
- Place foods in the appropriate storage areas, following any storage instructions on the label or box.
- Protect food from contamination by keeping it covered.
- Store food off the floor (on shelves or pallets).
- Use clean, dry containers and wrappers if food needs to be divided into smaller quantities or re-wrapped.
- Stack shelves carefully without overloading: leave enough space between goods for air to circulate freely.
- Keep storage areas clean and dry: clear up any spills immediately.
- Check food regularly and always before you use it.

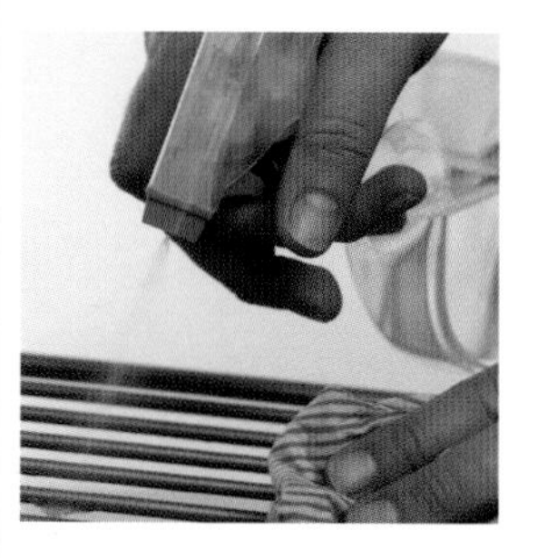

Keeping storage areas clean

- Rotate stock.
- Report to your supervisor any signs of pests.
- Separate any food that could be spoilt or has gone past its date mark – to ensure that it is not eaten – and tell your supervisor. He or she will tell you what to do once the food has been checked – for example, unacceptable food might be returned to the supplier or destroyed.
- Store cleaning chemicals and materials in separate, clearly labelled storage areas.

Use the stock with the shortest shelf life first

Key points

- Foods must be stored in appropriate storage areas set aside for the purpose.
- Storage areas must be kept clean and free from pests.

Stock rotation

Whenever you are asked to store food or to take something out of storage, you should rotate the stock. Stock rotation involves using a product with the shortest shelf life before using a similar product with a longer shelf life. When you store or display food, put the stock with the shortest shelf life at the front and place stock with the longest shelf life at the back. To remove food from storage or display, take the food from the front. Always check the date mark, packaging and condition of the food before use.

Key points

- The rotation of stock helps to ensure that food is eaten while it is safe, wholesome and at its best.
- Stock rotation involves using stock with the shortest shelf life first.

Foods for refrigerated storage

High-risk and perishable foods must be refrigerated because most food poisoning and spoilage bacteria do not multiply, or multiply very slowly, at refrigerator temperatures (0°C to 5°C).

Examples of foods to be refrigerated

- Raw meat, poultry and fish.
- Cooked meat, poultry, fish and seafood.
- Meat, poultry and fish products, such as pies and pâtés.
- The contents of opened cans of meat, fish and fruit, once they have been placed in suitable containers.
- Vacuum-packed raw meat, poultry and fish.
- Unopened pasteurized canned food, such as ham.
- Milk, dairy products and products containing them (for instance, a quiche).
- Anything labelled for refrigeration, such as bottled sauces without preservatives.
- Prepared salads.

Eggs should be kept in a refrigerator where there is space to do so and there is no risk of contamination. Otherwise, eggs should be kept in a cool store room. Some vegetables and fruit may be refrigerated if desired – they should be washed and separated from other foods.

Key point

- High-risk and perishable foods must be stored in refrigerators at 0°C to 5°C.

Stacking food in refrigerators

If possible, use *separate* refrigerators or cold stores for raw foods (such as meat and poultry) and for high-risk foods (such as dairy products and cooked meats). Where you have to use a multi-purpose refrigerator, always store raw meat and poultry on a shelf *below* other foods so that juices or blood cannot drip onto other foods and contaminate them.

Stack the shelves so that cold air can circulate and you can easily check the stock. Don't leave refrigerator doors open any longer than necessary because the temperature inside the refrigerator will rise. Never put hot food in a refrigerator. It raises the temperature of the refrigerator and may create condensation, which can cause contamination by dripping onto other food.

Protect refrigerated food from contamination

Store vacuum-packed meat, poultry and fish in a refrigerator

Safe frozen storage

Most micro-organisms are dormant at freezer temperatures (-18°C or below), so they cannot multiply. However, some bacteria or their spores survive and may start to multiply as soon as the food reaches temperatures in the danger zone. Frozen food should never be re-frozen once it has thawed or partly defrosted because of the increased risk of causing illness.

Stacking a freezer

Place raw foods below high-risk foods to avoid any risk of contamination. Place stock with the longest shelf life below stock with a short shelf life. Keep the food in the supplier's packing if it is clean and unbroken and always re-seal opened packaging. If the food needs to be re-wrapped, label the item clearly and include the date mark. Don't put unwrapped food in the freezer – it could become contaminated, cause contamination, or be damaged by freezer burn.

Wrap, label and date mark food before putting it in the freezer

Unwrapped food may be damaged by freezer burn

Key point

- Freezers should operate at -18°C or colder.

Storing dry and other goods

Dry goods must be kept in cool, dry and well-ventilated conditions. There must be sufficient space between supplies to allow air to flow freely and for you to check the goods. The food must be kept in secure packaging as many dry foods are attractive to pests. Although dry and canned goods have a long shelf life, you must take care to check and rotate the stock regularly.

Root vegetables, such as potatoes, need a cool, dark storage area. Make sure that soil does not contaminate other foods.

Dry goods must be kept in secure packaging

Root vegetables need a cool, dark storage area

Key point

- Dry goods must be kept in cool, dry and well-ventilated conditions.

Cleaning storage areas

All storage areas must be kept scrupulously clean to prevent contamination. Before you carry out cleaning (*see* Chapter 10), you must ensure that food is adequately covered and is maintained at an appropriate temperature.

Whenever possible, transfer refrigerated or frozen foods to other units while you clean. If there are insufficient refrigerator or freezer units available to do so, ensure that the food is thoroughly wrapped to keep refrigerated food out of the danger zone and to keep frozen food frozen. Replace the food as soon as possible.

Keep a close watch for signs of pest infestation (*see* Chapter 11) and follow your company rules for reporting problems and separating damaged food.

Key point

- All storage areas must be kept scrupulously clean to prevent contamination.

Protect food from contamination during cleaning

Summary

1. Food handlers have legal responsibilities to do everything possible to keep food safe and it is illegal to sell spoilt food.

2. Spoilage is the natural process of ageing, or deterioration, that makes food unacceptable to customers.

3. Spoilage is caused by spoilage bacteria, mould and yeast.

4. Spoilage can be accelerated by careless handling, inappropriate storage and pest infestation.

5. Preservation techniques are used to prolong the period when food is safe, appetising and nutritious to eat.

6. It is essential to be able to recognise the signs of spoilage.

7. Highly perishable foods must be labelled with a *use-by* date mark, while products with a longer shelf life must have a *best-before* date mark.

8. Deliveries of food should be checked for condition, temperature and shelf life.

9. Food should be stored immediately after checking a delivery. High-risk, perishable and frozen foods should be stored before other types of food because they need to stay out of the danger zone or remain frozen.

10. Foods must be stored in appropriate storage areas set aside for the purpose.

11. Storage areas must be kept clean and free from pests.

12. The rotation of stock helps to ensure that food is eaten while it is safe, wholesome and at its best.

13. Stock rotation involves using stock with the shortest shelf life first.

14. High-risk and perishable foods must be stored in refrigerators at 0°C to 5°C.

15. Freezers should operate at -18°C or colder.

16. Dry goods must be kept in cool, dry and well-ventilated conditions.

17. All storage areas must be kept scrupulously clean to prevent contamination.

Chapter 13
Preparing and presenting food

Regardless of the type of premises in which food is prepared, displayed, sold or served, the food must remain safe and wholesome. You may not be involved in all the activities mentioned in this chapter, but it is important to remember the general principles for food safety and to follow the rules at your workplace.

Key word

Core temperature – the temperature at the centre or the thickest part of food.

Preparing food

Food preparation involves a wide range of activities including washing, peeling, cutting, sieving, mixing, portioning, plating and decorating. Although methods and ingredients vary enormously, the food safety principles are the same.

Preparation principles

- Protect food from contamination at all times.
- Wear suitable, clean protective clothing.
- Wash your hands before working with food and regularly throughout the preparation period (see Chapter 8).
- Touch food by bare hand as little as possible.
- Use clean equipment and utensils.
- Clean and disinfect boards and utensils when you switch between raw foods and high-risk foods (see Chapter 10).
- Use the correct boards and utensils for the task – according to the colour-coding, for instance.
- Control time and temperature (see Chapter 7) and keep high-risk foods out of the danger zone.
- Plan your preparation so there is plenty of time for thorough thawing or cooling, for example, and so that food is not left lying around before sale or service.
- Work systematically to prevent cross-contamination.
- Use a fresh, clean spoon each time you need to taste-test food.

Key points

- Safeguard food by doing everything possible to:
  - prevent contamination
  - stop pathogens from multiplying
  - destroy pathogens.
- Control time and temperature and keep high-risk foods out of the danger zone.

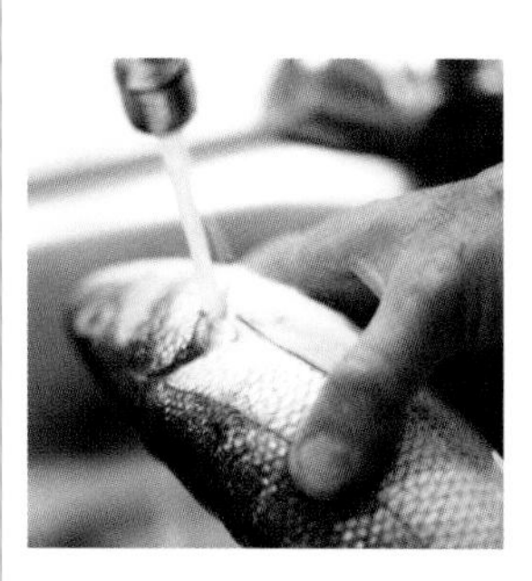

Wash raw fish before use

Thawing frozen food

Some foods may be safely cooked from frozen, provided that the manufacturer's instructions are followed. However, most raw frozen foods, such as meat and poultry, must be completely thawed before cooking.

Inadequate control of time and temperature often leads to illness. Frozen food enters the danger zone as it thaws, so the thawing time and the final temperature before cooking must be monitored carefully.

If large items, such as poultry or meat, are not thawed thoroughly before cooking starts, ice may remain at the centre. Although the heat cooks the food surface, the internal temperature may not be hot enough to destroy any pathogenic micro-organisms at the centre. In fact, the temperature deep in the food may be in the danger zone – ideal for bacterial multiplication.

Wherever possible, thawing should take place in a specially designed thawing cabinet, or in a refrigerator set aside for the purpose.

Methods of thawing

It is unsafe to thaw food at an ambient temperature, because the food is at a danger zone temperature. Depending on your company policy, the type and size of the food and the manufacturer's instructions, food may be thawed by one of the following methods:

- in a refrigeration unit at 5°C or colder, provided that various safety measures are observed (see below)
- in a microwave oven, provided that the manufacturer's instructions and recommendations are followed – for example, stirring or turning food part way through the process
- submerged under cold, running, potable (drinking quality) water.

Thaw frozen food carefully

Thawing principles

- Plan your work to take thawing times into account: remember that some foods can take a very long time to thaw completely.
- Use clean and disinfected equipment and utensils.
- Place the food in a container that will hold the thawing juices, without overflowing or dripping.
- Cover the food to prevent contamination during thawing.
- If using a multi-use refrigerator, place frozen food on the lowest shelf to prevent juices from dripping onto other foods and contaminating them.
- Select the most suitable thawing method according to the type and size of the food and the equipment available.
- Never re-freeze thawed food.

Key point

- Frozen food enters the danger zone as it thaws, so the thawing time and the final temperature before cooking must be monitored carefully.

Cooking

Quite apart from considerations of flavour, cooking is a good way to destroy pathogenic micro-organisms – provided that the food is cooked thoroughly. This involves ensuring that the food becomes hot enough all the way through for long enough to reduce pathogenic and spoilage micro-organisms to safe levels.

As a guide, most bacteria are destroyed at temperatures of 72°C or hotter when the core temperature is held for at least two minutes. You may find that your company asks you to cook some foods at a higher temperature.

Whenever possible, cut large joints and poultry into smaller portions to ensure that they cook evenly through to the centre. Cook stuffings separately so that they do not prevent the poultry or meat from cooking right through.

To ensure an even temperature throughout it may be necessary to turn food over part way through the cooking period, or to stir stews and casseroles. This is particularly important if you are using a microwave oven for prime cooking, because otherwise there may be cool spots at temperatures in the danger zone. Food cooked by microwave needs to stand for two minutes after cooking to allow the temperature to equalise throughout the food.

Always make the final check on the core temperature of food towards the end of the cooking period (or after the standing period for microwave-cooked foods). Even though the surface may be cooked, the centre of the food could remain in the danger zone (*see* Chapter 7).

Cooking principles

- Plan your work so that hot food is not prepared too far ahead of service.
- Rotate or turn over large food items part way through cooking and stir liquid foods frequently.
- Allow food cooked in a microwave oven to stand for two minutes after cooking, or for the period specified by the food's manufacturer.
- Measure the core temperature.
- Be certain that the food reaches at least the minimum temperature for the required time.

Key point

- Cook food thoroughly to destroy pathogenic micro-organisms.

Stir liquid food frequently

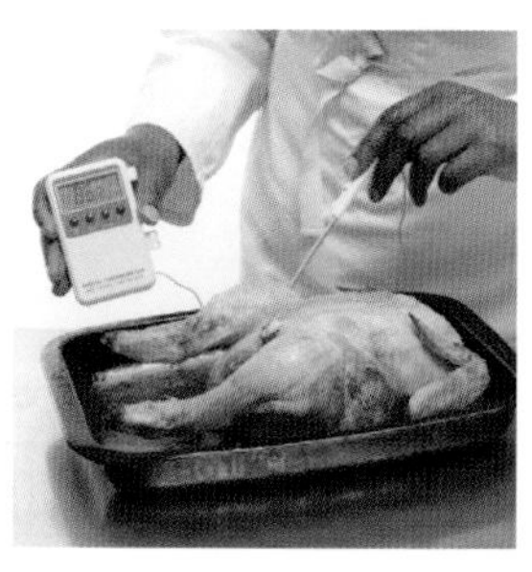

Measure the core temperature

Cooling hot food

Inadequate cooling is a major cause of food poisoning. The biggest problem is cooling food too *slowly*. Hot food has to pass through the danger zone as it cools. As a consequence, you must reduce the temperature as quickly as possible so the food is in the danger zone for the shortest possible period.

While the food is cooling, it must be protected from contamination.

Check the temperature of food as it cools and particularly near to the end of the estimated cooling period. Find out what the rules are in your company if the food is cooling too slowly.

Methods of cooling

The aim is to reduce the food temperature to 5°C or colder within 90 minutes, then to refrigerate it. This can be difficult to achieve without a blast chiller which shortens the time that food spends at danger zone temperatures. If a blast chiller is not available, there are other options that might be approved by your workplace:

- dividing the hot food into smaller or thinner portions
- placing the hot food in shallow pans to increase the surface area of the food which accelerates the cooling process – ideally the containers should allow the food to be only 50mm to 75mm deep
- using an ice bath – transfer the hot food to a clean, cold container and place that container in a larger one that holds ice or ice and water
- stirring, or rotating, food while it is cooling
- adding ice (made from potable water) as an ingredient.

Whenever possible, use large shallow trays and pans for cooling food in liquid, because the large surface area helps to accelerate the cooling. Remove cooked meat joints and whole chickens from their juices before placing them in clean containers with enough space for air to circulate.

Never place hot food in a refrigerator because the refrigerator temperature will rise, causing condensation that could contaminate other food. Never use a chiller cabinet or vending machine for cooling hot food because the equipment is not designed to reduce the temperature quickly enough.

Cooling principles

- Plan your work to take cooling times into account.
- Protect cooling food from contamination.
- Use a method of cooling that is approved by your workplace.
- Aim to reduce the core temperature to 5°C or cooler within 90 minutes.

Divide food to cool it quickly

Key point

- When cooling hot food you must reduce the temperature as quickly as possible so the food is in the danger zone for the shortest possible period.

Precautions for reheating food

Reheated food is also a common cause of food poisoning, so many companies ban reheating. Problems occur if the food is not heated sufficiently, particularly if the initial cooking, cooling and storage were inappropriate.

For example, if rice is boiled, then cooled or stored at an ambient temperature, spores of the bacterium *Bacillus cereus* may germinate and produce a toxin (a bacterial poison). If the rice is then reheated inadequately – say by flash frying – the toxin may not be destroyed.

If you are permitted to reheat food, never reheat a particular item more than once, and discard any left-overs of reheated food. Remove the food from the refrigerator just before reheating and serving and not any earlier. Always follow instructions on prepared food.

It is good practice to reheat food to a core temperature of at least 70°C for two minutes. To be on the safe side, the law in Scotland states that reheating must be to a minimum of 82°C. If food does not get hot enough, you will provide bacteria with an ideal temperature at which to multiply.

Reheating principles

- Ensure that food reaches the minimum temperature for at least the minimum time.
- Reheat food once only.
- Check the core temperature for the final time towards the end of reheating, or after the standing time for microwave-cooked foods.
- Discard uneaten reheated food.

Key point

- Reheated food is a common cause of food poisoning.

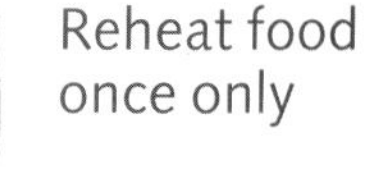

Reheat food once only

Discard uneaten reheated food

Hot and cold holding

Although the ideal is to cook or reheat food and serve or sell it straight away, in practice many companies need to keep prepared items hot or cold for a period before the food is consumed.

Hot holding

Cooked or reheated high-risk food which is not required for immediate consumption and is intended for eating hot, must be held at 63°C or above. In other words, it must be kept out of the danger zone. Before hot holding, the food must first reach the required minimum cooking or reheating temperature for the required time. Stir or rotate the food frequently to prevent cool spots occurring.

Cold holding

High-risk food intended for eating cold should be held at 5°C or colder – in other words, outside the danger zone and under refrigeration. Food that has previously been cooked should be cooled rapidly by an approved method before refrigerating.

Hot and cold holding principles

- Keep hot food hot – at 63°C or hotter.
- Keep cold food cold – at 5°C or cooler.
- Check the temperature regularly to ensure that the food is not in the danger zone.

Key points

- Keep hot food really hot, at 63°C or hotter.
- Keep cold food really cold, ideally at 5°C or cooler.

Keep hot food at 63°C or above

Keep cold food at 5°C or cooler

Displaying food

Food displayed for sale or service must be protected against all sources of contamination. Packaged food must be securely wrapped and labelled. Open food must be covered by lids, or protected by a sneeze guard.

In self-service areas, there should be utensils available so that customers are less likely to touch the food by hand. The utensils should be replaced regularly by clean ones.

If you have to weigh raw meat, poultry, fish or any high-risk food, place a clean sheet of food paper (deli paper) on the weighing platform first. This helps to prevent cross contamination, but is not a substitute for proper cleaning and disinfection.

Principles for displaying food

- Protect food from contamination.
- Replace self-service utensils with clean, sanitised ones regularly.
- Measure the temperature of food frequently and follow the workplace procedures if there is an unsatisfactory temperature reading.

Food being displayed for sale or service must be protected from contamination

Summary

1. Safeguard food by doing everything possible to:
   - prevent contamination
   - stop pathogens from multiplying
   - destroy pathogens.
2. Control time and temperature and keep high-risk foods out of the danger zone.
3. Frozen food enters the danger zone as it thaws, so the thawing time and the final temperature before cooking must be monitored carefully.
4. Cook food thoroughly to destroy pathogenic micro-organisms.
5. When cooling hot food you must reduce the temperature as quickly as possible so the food is in the danger zone for the shortest possible period.
6. Reheated food is a common cause of food poisoning.
7. Keep hot food really hot, at 63°C or hotter.
8. Keep cold food really cold, ideally at 5°C or cooler.

Chapter 14
Food safety control

Food safety laws are designed to protect consumers from illness and harm. There is a recognised system – HACCP – for assessing food hazards, for introducing appropriate controls and for monitoring and maintaining standards. There are also special standards, referred to as codes of practice, for various sectors of the food industry, as well as rules within individual businesses. This chapter gives an overview of legal requirements.

Key words

Control or control measure – an action designed to eliminate or reduce a hazard to a recognised safe level.

Enforcement officer – a professional, usually an environmental health officer (EHO) or a trading standards officer, who enforces legislation covering food.

Food handler – anyone whose work involves food, or whose action or inaction could compromise the safety of food.

HACCP – Hazard Analysis and Critical Control Point, a formal system of hazard analysis and risk assessment designed to help food companies to deal with threats to food safety.

Legislation – laws and regulations.

Food handlers and the law

Everyone who deals with food as part of his or her work has a legal responsibility to safeguard food. Other people whose work could affect food safety, such as cleaners, also have legal responsibilities to protect food from contamination. The extent of your legal obligations depends upon your work activities and your role within the company where you work. You must find out how legislation affects you.

Generally speaking, the food legislation states that food handlers must:

- keep themselves clean
- keep their workplace clean
- wear suitable clean, washable protective clothing
- do everything possible to protect food from contamination
- store, prepare and display food at safe temperatures
- tell their employer if they have symptoms of food poisoning or certain other illnesses or conditions.

The laws also usually say that food handlers must not:

- do anything that would expose food to contamination
- sell food that is unfit for human consumption
- sell food with an expired date mark
- work with food if they have symptoms of food poisoning, or any other illness with similar symptoms, until their employer or doctor says it is safe to do so.

Key points

- Keep yourself and your workplace clean.
- Wear suitable clean, washable protective clothing.
- Protect food from contamination.
- Restrict the time that high-risk foods are left at danger zone temperatures.
- Tell your employer if you have symptoms of food poisoning or a food-borne illness.

Employers and the law

Proprietors (owners and employers) and anyone who is in charge of food premises, such as company directors and managers, have wider-ranging legal responsibilities than food handlers. Included in their responsibilities are ensuring that:

- the premises are registered with the local enforcement authority
- the premises are designed, equipped and operated in ways which prevent contamination and anything that could lead to illness or injury
- there are adequate washing facilities and arrangements for personal hygiene
- staff are appropriately trained and supervised
- create procedures to analyse food hazards and to eliminate or minimise the risks from those hazards to food safety.

Training

Your employer must ensure that you are trained to do the work involved in your job. The training must be appropriate to the tasks you carry out and a record should be kept of the type of training, the topics covered and the dates the training took place.

The way you are trained could include a mixture of formal and informal instruction and could take place at your usual workplace or elsewhere, such as a training centre. Your training might, for example, include simple demonstrations when someone shows you how to do something at work, informal advice while you are working and structured training sessions away from your workplace.

Key point

- You must be trained to carry out your work tasks.

Minimising risk

Food businesses are required by law to have procedures based on HACCP principles. HACCP stands for Hazard Analysis and Critical Control Point. It is a well-tested system that helps food businesses to ensure that everything that *should* happen in the workplace to protect food safety *does* indeed take place. In other words, HACCP is designed to help food companies to minimise the risk (likelihood of harm) from food hazards (possibility of harm from food).

To set up and run a HACCP system food companies need to:

- analyse the hazards to food safety at every stage of food handling in that particular business
- assess the level of risk from each hazard
- decide the most critical points at which there must be food safety controls – this could be the time and temperature control for cooking a joint of meat, for example
- implement appropriate controls for eliminating hazards, if this is possible, or reducing the risk from each hazard to the lowest possible level
- establish a monitoring system to ensure that the controls are effective – what should happen does happen
- set up procedures to correct any food safety problems
- review the system from time to time and whenever operations change.

Key point

- HACCP is designed to help food companies to minimise the risk (likelihood of harm) from food hazards (possibility of harm from food).

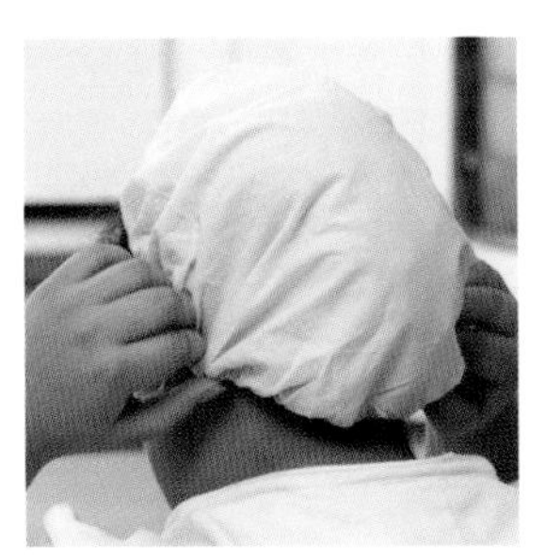

Follow the rules at your workplace

Follow good hygiene practices

Protect food from contamination

You and food safety control

HACCP systems are usually set up and managed by specialists, managers, supervisors or teams of people from throughout the business. *You* could be involved in a range of actions that play an essential part in running the system – for instance, probing a joint of meat and recording the temperature on a record sheet.

Whatever your work involves, you will play an important part in food safety control by:

- following the rules at your workplace
- protecting food from contamination
- keeping yourself clean and having hygienic habits
- following the basic rules of time and temperature control
- spotting food hazards
- reporting faults, problems, risks and any worries you have about food safety to your supervisor.

Key points

- Carry out your part in hazard spotting.
- Follow instructions and rules at work.
- Report all food hazards, faults and suspicions of contamination.

Enforcement

The enforcement of food safety legislation is carried out by specialists who are employed by the local authority or port authority. They usually have the job title of environmental health officer (EHO) or trading standards officer. The enforcement officers give advice and assistance to food businesses as well as ensuring that food companies obey the law. They have the power to:

- enter and inspect food premises
- investigate outbreaks of food poisoning, food-borne illness and possible offences
- remove suspect food and have it destroyed if it is considered to be unsafe to eat
- take companies to court for breaking food safety laws.

You should always co-operate with enforcement officers because they are aiming to prevent illness. You might commit an offence if you obstruct their inquiries.

Key point

- Co-operate with enforcement officers.

Diligence

Food companies can avoid breaking the law by ensuring *due diligence* (reasonable care). Your work towards food safety helps to ensure that the company is diligent.

Penalties

If a court decides that the law has been broken, it can set various penalties. Breaking a food safety law can result in:

- a fine
- a prison sentence
- closure of the business
- a ban on an owner or manager from working in the food business
- a criminal record.

Breaking the law could also result in a business being order to pay civil compensation to customers affected by unsafe food.

Summary

1. Keep yourself and your workplace clean.

2. Wear suitable clean, washable protective clothing.

3. Protect food from contamination.

4. Restrict the time that high-risk foods are left at danger zone temperatures.

5. Tell your employer if you have symptoms of food poisoning or a food-borne illness.

6. You must be trained to carry out your work tasks.

7. HACCP is designed to help food companies to minimise the risk (likelihood of harm) from food hazards (possibility of harm from food).

8. Carry out your part in hazard spotting.

9. Follow instructions and rules at work.

10. Report all food hazards, faults and suspicions of contamination.

11. Co-operate with enforcement officers.

Index

Design: www.red-stone.com
Illustration: Ned Jolliffe
Photography: Andrew Olney

Except pages 3 (Medioimages/Punchstock), 8T (David Scharf/Science Photo Library), 11 (Photodisc/Punchstock), 13T (Graham Day/Anthony Blake), 13B (foodcollection.com/PunchStock), 14 (Larry Dale Gordon/Getty Images), 15 (Photodisc/Punchstock), 17T (Tim Hill/Anthony Blake), 17C(Designpics/ Punchstock), 17B (Joff Lee/Anthony Blake), 18T (Stockbyte/Punchstock), 18B (Hans Strand/Getty Images), 19R (John Sims/Anthony Blake), 21L (Prof. C.R. Madeley/Science Photo Library), 21R (Alfred Pasieka/Science Photo Library), 22 (Isabelle Rozenbaum/PhotoAlto/Getty Images), 26 Charlie Stebbings/Anthony Blake), (Deximage/Punchstock), (Teubner/Getty Images) and (Maximillian Stock Ltd/Anthony Blake), 29 (digitalvision/Getty Images), 34B (Bigshots/Imagebank/Getty Images), 37 (Clare Parker/Anthony Blake), 38 (Foodcollection/Getty Images), 39RT (Rita Maas/Getty Images), 39RB (Ryan McVay/Photodisc Green/Getty Images), 50T (Mel Yates/Photodisc Red/Getty Images), 50C (David De Lossy/Photodisc Green/Getty Images), 50B (John Carey/Anthony Blake), 52 (Jessamyn Harris/Getty Images), 53T (Image Source/Getty Images), 53C (Nick Koudis/Photodisc Green/Getty Images), 53B (Julia Fullerton-Batten/Getty Images), 55 (Comstock/Punchstock), 57T (John A Rizzo/Photodisc Green/Getty Images), 57B (VEER Louis Wallach/ Getty Images), 58B (Alex Wilson/digitalvision/Getty Images), 62T (Stockbyte Platinum/Alamy), 67 (Alex Wilson/digitalvision/Getty Images), 70T (Brand X Pictures/Punchstock), 70B (Robin Redfern/Ecoscene), 71T (Robin Redfern/ Ecoscene), 71B (TNT Magazine/Alamy), 74T (Tim Hill/Anthony Blake), 74C (Anthony Blake/Anthony Blake), 74LB (Steve Taylor/digitalvision/Getty Images), 75 (Kevin Summers/Getty Images), 78B (Dejan/fStop/Getty Images), 80T (Raimund Koch/Getty Images), 80B (Ryan McVay/Photodisc Green/Getty Images), 81RT (Lenora Gim/Getty Images), 81RB (PhotoLink/Photodisc Green/Getty Images), 85 (Studio Adna/Anthony Blake), 87T (Matthew Septimus/Getty Images), 89 (digitalvision/Punchstock), 90 (Eaglemoss Consumer Publications/Anthony Blake) and (Dominic Dibbs/Anthony Blake), 91 (Dominic Dibbs/Anthony Blake).

Shoot location: Food Studies Department,
Southwark College, London

Print: The Astron Group
Stock: Era Silk, 50% post-consumer waste and 50% TCF pulp